Praise

✪ An indescribable account of the evil aspect of the planned pandemic. The intentional murder of the unvaccinated is beyond evil. I, too, got emotional watching this. Somehow we need to get the unwashed masses to understand what is really going on. So many terrible stories of iatrogenesis—death by doctors rather than by disease. We run the risk of death from doctors shaming and scaring people into having the vaccines or death by a vengeful doctor if we are not vaccinated and end up ill in the hospital. —JJ

✪ Great writing. As a retired MD (Oncology, Immunology) that knew the Plandemic was BS about two weeks in and watched everything in medicine get corrupted, I relate to everything here. —SR, MD

✪ Sir Robert: The good thing about COVID is the unbelievable web of lies that holds big Pharma together is being exposed. We do not have a medical system. We have a drug dispensing system. There is a sickening level of depravity that we are seeing exposed. Thank you for your ability to write about these crimes. What a journey! It continues. You offer hope. 🙏 —JM

✪ You have insight, rare in this present world. Keep trying to relate to the ones around you. We must keep trying to rescue as many as possible while the lifeboat is still available to them... Whether THEY choose to come aboard is their choice, we only have a responsibility to ensure they know that THIS Is Not A Dress Rehearsal! —SD

✪ We are run by spiders, not the ones of nature, but self-created psychopathic spiders spinning shiny intricate webs to lure, ensnare, and feed upon their unsuspecting fellow humans. The web is far-reaching, connecting 'science,' finance, medicine, and the creation of new moralities untethered from the past. Once lured in, it is hard to escape unless you are too big and heavy for the web to sustain its grip. Dr. Yoho's book is a way to expand; it is a way to give weight to your thoughts that things are not right. With study, you will be too big and heavy and fall through the web and escape. Look at the book as an elementary primer that is simple but sophisticated. — Contributor EC

✪ This is greater than humanity and is a spiritual war!!!! —JB

✪ You are an EXCELLENT writer... I so enjoyed reading through your real-life experiences. That climbing photo will give me nightmares tonight though haha! —AN

✪ Humans with medical degrees that exercise your degree of self-reflection are rare. Respect bro. High Five. :). —ML

✪ You are doing us all a great service by speaking out and whistle-blowing about the problems with medicine and healthcare. This is waking others up not to trust what the system tells us about covid. —PR

✪ You've climbed the highest mountains—you're on top. YS

✪ During most of the pandemic, my current doctor constantly begged me to get the Jab, and I had to explain to him repeatedly why I would never do so. Now he's uncharacteristically subdued and quiet. He asks me about my experience with ivermectin each time I see him. He finally knows what some of us knew all along. —MC

✪ Wow! What a life you have had so far! Now it looks like the next chapter may involve writing... more, please! 🙏. —CG

✪ You're a gifted storyteller. Keep it up! —JN

✪ This is an excellent essay about the predators among and above us. —IT

✪ Our salvation is in each other. We are our heroes. When I start to feel discouraged, I read the lists of health freedom doctors, lawyers, journalists, whistleblowers, etc., that I've been compiling for 1.5 years. I consult the websites of the many organizations they start to support the uninjected, the injured, and the families of those who have died. Take the exasperation and grief you feel and look for evidence of those among us using their powers for good. So many good things are happening. —JO

✪ Amazing that despite the content of your article, it was calming to listen to. Thank you for explaining your experiences and thoughts about our awful situation as a nation. We moved out of a blue state a few years ago to another mostly rural state where we have more family ties. We have been preparing for what may come our way. My six-year-old grandson saw our garage and how full the shelves were of food and water. So it was an opportunity to make him aware of how we must get more self-sufficient. We have also bought an outdoor fire pit for cooking. We want to know people who sell food, wood, and other items. We also have the necessary items for self-defense and bartering. For us to be prepared has taken the burden of fear off our shoulders. —RZ

✪ Well, that was interesting to hear the surgeon's point of view about the transgender industry that he is engaged in. I started hearing about this subject a few years ago when my sister's stepdaughter started helping her three daughters to transfer themselves to be male. It was shocking to me. I was considered a Tom Boy when I was a young girl because I grew up on a farm doing work that was considered for males. Plus, I liked hanging out with males at that time. I also knew that males had the advantage over women in so many areas of life. I never wished to be male, even though I had a hard time being around groups of females, and I still do to this day. —MP

✪ Excellent work you've done here on Substack. I am so pleased to be a subscriber and appreciate all you have endured to reach this stage. You can now share your messages, wisdom, knowledge, and desire to persevere to help inspire strength in others who are confronting unthinkable horrors of the world we now live in. Thank you for your courage! —NJ

✪ I'm glad to hear my feelings confirmed by a doctor like you. Your remarks lend credence to trusting my gut. Thank you! 🙏 Oh, and I'm staying clear of doctors (nothing against you, you are a gem and a seeming rarity)... The last time I saw one was summer of 2019 (GYN). Just before that Dr. retired, then my other Dr. (Int.) retired a few months later (both early), then another Dr. (Opth). retired a few months later... further confirmation for me to trust my judgment. I feel like I'm in a bit of a holding pattern. I've found I have to trust that. I've had so many signs in my past to "Stay away!". I'm listening and watching for guidance continually. Thanks again for yours! 🙏🙏😊. —MT

✪ I thoroughly enjoy your writing. As someone who interacts with HCP to earn a living, I deeply appreciate your SS. I feel her words to my core. I'm stunned and shrinking inwards more and more. What I see of healthcare with eyes wide open is worse than any horror film or book I've read. This is in real-time. Unfortunately, it's steering me toward my old patterns of PTSD and dissociation. Which I believe many who haven't had it DO NOW! Most, if not all, healthcare workers are injected with cognitive impairment. We are in a serious situation, and I don't want to be in any hospital. They make everyone wear masks and limit visitors, yet they don't want people to be angry. This is against our instincts - or my instincts. Thank you for the book suggestions! —WR

✪ I JUST told my husband (and a neighbor I'm trying to black-pill) that I feel like I'm in an alternate universe. My trip to the grocery store was depressing and chilling: zombies in masks and others walking around sipping Starbucks like nothing's out of the ordinary — it's Friday! Where's Happy Hour? All while these psychopaths plan a future of Hell, the rest of the world is plunged into economic depression and violence. I'm in LA, so I have a front-row seat. —KC

✪ Thank You for your contribution to making this a genuinely advancing civilization! Earth is wobbling on its axis & you are one of the few keeping it from tipping over! —JB

✪ [About the Accutane disaster story] I'm horrified. Thank you for sharing this testimony, and my heart grieves for this brilliant young woman. Both my daughters were treated with Accutane in high school. They seem to be fine, but who ever really knows? I would be interested to know of any other diet/lifestyle or medications that would help scarring cystic acne because it is very difficult for young women who end up with scarring on their faces. —TJ

✪ [From a nurse anesthetist] Never EVER would I anesthetize a traumatized boy/girl or woman/man for a surgeon to perform any type [of transgender] butcher surgeries that forever will alter their appearance. It is so abhorrent that it almost gives me red rashes. People who want to undergo these surgeries are being influenced and groomed for a long time before they 'decide' to take the jump into a forever medicalized world. —CM

About the cover

In Greek mythology, Cassandra was a Trojan priestess admired by the god Apollo. He sought to win her love by giving her the power to see the future. In exchange, she promised her favors to him, but she changed her mind. Apollo was enraged, but he could not revoke his gift, so he added the curse that no-one would believe her.

A "Cassandra" now refers to someone whose prophecies—generally of impending disaster—are not believed.

Robert Yoho's other writing

A New Body in One Day (2004)

Butchered by "Healthcare" (2020)

Hormone Secrets (2021).

Twenty articles in medical journals

Cosmetic surgery website: I retired in 2019 but DrYoho.com is still live

Author website: RobertYohoAuthor.com

Please subscribe to RobertYoho.substack.com to stay up to date.

Cassandra's Memo

COVID and the Global Psychopaths

Robert Yoho, MD (ret)

Inverness Press

Cover design by the amazing Callum Jagger. The image was from HERE. Megan Khalil helped with other issues. Contact Upwork.com to work with either of them.

Anyone may copy any chapter of this book word for word and republish them—as long as they give proper attribution and the copy remains free. To reiterate, you may republish the article as long as it is appropriately credited and unaltered. I never charge a fee for linking or copying my content. If you want to use it in any other way, ask me. I have not turned anyone down yet.

I write solely to educate and report news to my readers. I donate what little I make here to our movement's leaders.

Disclaimer: These are my opinions and general commentary. It is not medical or other advice. I retired from practice and resigned from my medical license, so I cannot treat you, anyway. This should assure you that my conflicts of interest are minimal. Your healthcare providers are the only ones who can be responsible for your care and advise you about treatment. Vet them, be respectful, but never surrender your critical thinking powers.

I have no financial relationship with any caregiver or institution or received funding from anyone. I own no substantial healthcare stock nor do I get paid by corporate sources.

I do not render legal, investment, accounting, or other professional services. While I have used my best efforts in preparing this book, I make no representations or warranties concerning its accuracy or completeness. I disclaim any implied warranties of merchantability or fitness for a particular purpose. No warranty may be created or extended by sales representatives or written sales materials. The advice and strategies contained herein may not be suitable for your situation. You should consult with a professional when appropriate. Use this information at your own risk. I am not liable for any loss of profit or other commercial damages, including but not limited to special, incidental, consequential, personal, or other damages.

RobertYohowriter@gmail.com POB 50007, Pasadena, California, 91115

Ebook ISBN: 978-1-7354857-7-5

Print ISBN: 978-1-7354857-8-2BISAC

Subject Codes:

To the great heroes in our freedom movement.
You know who you are.

Contents

If you know the enemy and know yourself, you need not fear the result of a hundred battles.

— Sun Tzu

Preface: How I Got the Memo

This photo is from 2015, but I like it better than today's.

Life's most painful, challenging, and imperative work is shedding illusions. I know—I understood less than half of the contents here two years ago. Since then, I have been setting fire to my preconceptions and burning them to the ground. It has been agonizing.

Getting others to see through deceptions is far more difficult. Emerson wrote, "A man is what he thinks about all day long." We are inside the most pervasive and effective propaganda campaign in history, and there is a lot of denial —even as the world races into totalitarianism. Those who have spent years feeding their brains with mainstream media are putting their thumbs in their ears.

Despite all this, many people know what is happening, and more are learning. After someone awakens, they never go back to sleep. This book is your chance to boost your skepticism, find uncensored sources, and catch up. When more understand the truth, our injured US Constitution has the power to crush the conspirators.

To survive during our distressing and depressing age, you must face the facts. Only one path works: *you must ignore authorities and look at the data yourself.* If you do not, you are inevitably making decisions based on what you are told by censors and paid-off or deluded "experts." I present information and give references, but you must evaluate it. I am not a climatologist, a vaccinologist, a mathematician— nor a licensed physician anymore—but I studied full-time for five years to learn the truths in my books.

We are living through a Greek tragedy, but few realize that each calamity is planned for a purpose. Today's theft, lies, and the explosion of immoral and illegal activity are neither random nor spontaneous. A few thousand "psychopaths," working in a loose alliance, are driving it. Psychiatry neutered this name to "sociopaths," but the original is a better fit. Learning about these deviants is a black pill, an icy reality. They stalk among us, nearly invisible behind a wall of lies, but their actions reveal them.

Although psychopaths desire riches, this is not their core agenda. I uncover their motives and teach you to identify them in Chapter 2. It reads like fiction, but remember that we have recently been through the unthinkable. You need this information to understand current events and know what to do next.

This is a workbook about our world from many points of view. Study the chapters and references that most apply to your situation. The only required reading is Parts One, Two, and Ten. This last describes the leaders of the supposed "Great Reset." Knowledgeable people might only need to skim the rest.

To give you breathing space away from the story's savagery, I put "Diversion" chapters at the end of each Part describing my origin story. You can skip them, but trust me, you will need a few breaks.

For much of this book, I use the work of some of the best minds alive, polymaths all. They are the people who sent me warning "memos" over the last 18 months. I would never have understood much without their help and stand in awe of what they are accomplishing. I am merely synthesizing and spreading their messages, but all errors here are mine.

Thank you for your service. You are courageous, and your contributions are far greater than mine. You are Joseph Mercola, RFK, Jr., Naomi Wolf, Pierre Kory, CJ Hopkins, Patrick Moore, Alex Epstein, Craig Paardekooper, Toby Rogers, 2nd Smartest Guy in the World, Steve Kirsch, Unbekoming, A Midwestern Doctor, Ronald Stein, Christian Elliot, Tess Lawrie, Tim and May Hindmarsh, Nick Yaya, David Carmichael, Silvia Cattori, Roberto Strongman, Vera Sharav, Peter McCormack, Bryce Eddy, Chaval, and others. EC, Tony Cecala, and Grant Horner edited. We are in this together—and this is not a Marxist slogan.

The authors' writing styles and skills in this compendium vary. Pierre Kory, for example, communicates in the terse way that he must use for patient notes. Mercola and his team have the most content, but their essays are long and read like outlines, so skim them. Naomi Wolf has published bestsellers and tells her stories beautifully. Other authors must be crying as they write, and readers sense it.

Amazon's censors refused to publish *Cassandra's Memo*, so please write your reviews (thank you!) on other platforms such as Google, Kobo, Apple, or Barnes and Noble.

About the price: since Troy's original Cassandra never charged for her warnings, I do not, either. If I make anything after the returns and other book publishing idiocies, I will donate it to our movement's leaders. You may download the ebook for whatever price works for you at https://dl.bookfunnel.com/t2feeen29q. From booksellers, the ebook price minimum seems to be $.99, and $.40 is all mine. The physical book retails for about $30., and $2.10 per copy goes to my donation fund.

The references for *Cassandra's Memo* are available as links in the ebook. I originally published most of the chapters at RobertYoho.Substack.com, which has these plus the audio. You can access these posts from the ebook with the "SUBSTACK LINK." In the print edition, use the QR codes with your cellphone camera.

Because Substack does not censor, it is worth more dead than alive, and some predator may buy it and pull the plug. If you stay on the RobertYoho.substack.com subscriber list, I will make the content available to you on another platform if this happens.

Presents for readers: If you buy my books—*thank you!*—Amazon will prioritize your reviews. But if you are short on funds or are a paid subscriber to robertyoho. substack.com, email me at robertyoho@substack.com or

Yoho.Robert@gmail.com, and I will gift my other ebooks to you.

The audio version of the first half of *Butchered by "Healthcare"* is published as a free podcast HERE and on YouTube. You can also listen to the first half of *Hormone Secrets* on YouTube HERE.

I have been a guest on hundreds of podcasts. THIS one is about hormone supplementation. A hormone testimonial video is HERE. One about healthcare corruption is HERE, and THIS is an introduction to this book.

Subscribe to RobertYoho.substack.com, and I will send you updates. RobertYohoAuthor.com has more.

All my best,

Robert Yoho, MD (ret), Yoho.robert@gmail.com

November 2022

For power readers: These will help you decipher anything.

1. *The updated Golden Rule* is that those with the gold make the rules, so learning the funding source explains a lot. I used to think it explained everything until I understood psychopaths. Read chapter 2 to learn about them.

2. *If you do not follow the reasoning, it is a clue that someone may be lying to sell you something.* Remember that you are just as bright as lawyers, doctors, Ph.D.s, and financial advisors. And even if they are honest, these eggheads are at a disadvantage—they are so lost in the weeds that they seldom see the entire picture.

3. *Confusion, controversy, and contradictory evidence about small numbers prove that any*

study is worthless. Never conclude "reasonable people disagree," "the science is developing," or that tiny percentage differences mean anything. Your default should be to disbelieve whatever you are told, for as Theodore Sturgeon's law states, "90 percent of everything is crap."

4. This garbage percentage is still higher for medical studies—and more recently, for "climate change" research. Why? Researchers must produce the results that funding sources command. Roughly 75 percent of worldwide health research financing is corrupt money from the Gates Foundation, the Wellcome Trust, and Fauci's NIAID agency. Want more proof? Richard Smith, editor of the *British Medical Journal* until 2004, titled his 2021 editorial, "Time to Assume That Health Research is Fraudulent Until Proven Otherwise." *Until proven otherwise.* RFK, Jr.'s book *The Real Anthony Fauci* presents staggering evidence Smith is correct.

5. *Although "link rot" destroys up to ten percent of the Internet's content each year, virtually everything ever posted is still alive and well on the Wayback Machine Internet archive.* Not even the Chinese or the global psychopaths have so far been able to hide from it. To find a hidden link, copy the bad URL (the web address at the top of the browser) and enter it at archive.org. Then look for the backed-up copies and select the date you want to view. You can save any page for free indefinitely on another of their pages. Unfortunately, the Wayback may

soon be vandalized or even destroyed. See Mercola's Fake Fact Checking in Part 2 to learn more.

6. *Blasting through certain paywalls is easy.* Sci-hub is a "piracy" website in Russia that can get you many academic articles at no charge. Just copy the link into their browser. This is against US law, but some academics publicly thank them. Whether you pay for articles is a private matter between you, the journal, Sci-hub, and your maker. My opinion is that all information —of any kind—should be shared freely.

Part One
Witness to Apocalypse

Chapter 1
Why Believe Me?

I was a cosmetic surgeon for most of my career. This narrow area had limited contact with the rest of medical practice. Its rumor of glamor was dubious, and the pay was overrated, but I liked the independence, and the work was rewarding.

This has images from my (mostly) virtual trips around the world, including a real polar bear.

* * *

SUBSTACK LINK

HERE IS HOW I woke up and became a modern-day Rip Van Winkle after running on the doctor treadmill for a lifetime.

In my final years of practice, most of my patients were women over 50 with depression and anxiety who thought cosmetic surgery would make them feel better. Most plastic surgeons operate on a string of these people without considering why they are so miserable. My patients trusted me, I wanted to help them, and I concluded after study that they were almost all hormone deficient. I began to offer appropriate candidates replacement therapy even if they decided against surgery. This made them feel great and improved their health.

I could not understand why these natural drugs were claimed to cause cancer, blood clotting, and heart disease. Hormones were inexpensive and highly beneficial; we had studied most of them for over eighty years. I learned that the FDA, acting in concert with big Pharma, had criminally distorted hormone prescribing standards by putting undeserved "black box warnings" on the drugs. This aggressive smear was being used to protect Pharma's profitable patent medications. This had sabotaged our elders. For more about this system, see the note at the end of this chapter.

My interests gradually broadened to include corruption in the rest of medicine. Because of corporate and government interference, money dominated every consideration, and patients were being injured and killed. Once I understood, I felt compelled to explain what I had learned, so I wrote *Hormone Secrets* and *Butchered by "Healthcare."* I finished these as I retired three years ago.

After nearly four years of writing and promoting these books, I found myself on a podcast with Dr. Peter Breggin. I wanted to talk about healthcare corruption, but he insisted we focus on Covid. I thought at first that Breggin was either a jerk or a little demented, but I was wrong.

As he confronted me, I felt like virtual reality glasses were being ripped from my head. After the interview was over, I began to study. I learned that evil forces had been battering our institutions and tearing America apart. Laws were being ignored, and the worst criminals were winning. Government and monster corporations were working in a fascist alliance similar to those in Japan during World War II. It was the corruption I wrote about in *Butchered,* writ large.

As I looked around, I saw:

✪ Things were so far gone that, at first, all seemed lost. Filthy rich companies were using lies as weapons, pressing perverse agendas and destroying our constitution.

✪ There was still time to act because some of our institutions still survived.

✪ The culture had undergone a shocking degeneration. "Woke" ideologies such as sexual confusion and bizarre, divisive racial theories were everywhere. I thought these were juvenile bad jokes confined to college campuses, but I learned that they had captured the left wing, the media, and most academics. Corporations were complying and profiting.

✪ China was buying our land and financing our social degradation. It was an open war. (Part 10).

✪ Institutions that I previously respected, such as hospitals, had turned predatory and had lost all regard for human life.

✪ A few people were standing up, but most were either hypnotized by the propaganda or trying to save themselves by covering their heads and pretending to agree.

✪ I soon realized that petting a rabid dog would never work—we had to fight.

By now, I have been swimming through this mess for several years. I read, write, and podcast 40 to 70 hours a week. Besides the US, I have traveled virtually to France, Taiwan, Britain, Dubai, India, Australia, and several Eastern Europe and African countries. I have made many friends.

My job is to get the memo out, but it is up to you to read and spread it.

* * *

My convictions

✪ We are nothing if we do not put others first.

✪ My standard is kaizen and praxis. Kaizen is Japanese for continuous improvement, and praxis in Greek means taking action.

✪ Individual rights are foundational. I hate the fostered dependency and collectivist nightmares sweeping the world today.

Since physicians have little time to come up for air, philosophies like these are nearly meaningless to us. Our lives devolve into Groundhog Days repeated ad nauseam. Between patient care, staff management, medical records, financial worries, and many other hassles, work consumes us. Our personal and intellectual development stands still for decades, and our patient-first ethic fades. Many are reduced to getting their continuing education from drug representatives.

I was once proud of being a doctor, but that is gone. Pride is at least a vanity and, at worst, a deadly sin. Losing it was for the best.

Since I am 69 years old, I face other challenges. Some of my friends are dying—more than a few from the vax. I see my end coming at me like a wall. I take no comfort from religion but find meaning in getting good work done in whatever time I have left.

* * *

Note

From *Butchered by "Healthcare."*

The immensely wealthy and powerful pharmaceutical companies have become increasingly entitled and emboldened over the past three decades. The FDA requires drug studies for patent approval, so "contract research groups" do trials that spoil science and make questionable medications look good. Mathematicians massage the numbers and bury data that do not support the drugs. Industry employees then write up the trials and send them to the FDA. Since more than half of the regulator's funding comes directly from corporations, approval is rarely an obstacle.

After the FDA gives permission to sell the drug, corporate ghostwriters spin articles for publication. Then the companies pay prominent physicians to affix their names as authors, and medical journal editors with financial conflicts approve them. Since the journals are primarily funded by the drug industry, publication is nearly automatic. The prestigious authors and publications lend credibility to questionable drugs, devices, and physician practices.

While this happens, physician opinion leaders with transparent financial conflicts such as research grants create prescribing guidelines that minimize risks and exaggerate benefits. These standards of practice are poorly grounded in science, but they authoritatively command practicing doctors how and when to use drugs.

The subsequent marketing campaign goes directly to the public and to individual physicians. Few observers believe either is appropriate, but the former is worse. Along with this, another favored strategy is corporate-funded advocacy groups that disease-monger. This involves spinning horror stories that spread fear to sell drugs.

Chapter 2
In the Company of Psychopaths

Gates, Schwab, Soros, Fauci, Trudeau, Pelosi, the
Chinese leaders, and a few thousand others get an "A" on
the psychopath test.

— Sherman, my anonymous contributor

These transnational criminals live to cheat, defraud, and blackmail. Many are killers. They make no contribution to those around them or society, and fair value exchange is foreign to them. They crave power and wealth, but this is secondary to their primary motivation—damaging others. Lies, conspiracies, and intimidation are their trademarks.

Today's agendas are so dark that they could only have been conceived and carried out by psychopaths. Their stated plan is "ending overpopulation," but this supposed problem is already solved. Global birth rates are crashing, and demographics prove that our numbers will peak and decline within a few decades. The Earth's people are now mostly fed, and their economic situation is improving.

9

So why the fraud? *Population reduction is killing and destruction for its own sake, which is what psychopaths hunger for.* Normal humans have trouble conceiving of such evil, see this behavior as irrational, and dismiss these people as crazy or "psychotic." This is inaccurate. Psychopaths see reality but have no "operating system" of human love, ethics, and sympathetic feelings.

SUBSTACK LINK

With this in mind, our world-gone-mad and all the lies make sense. The following schemes are designed to harm people *as the primary goal.*

- Covid is a purpose-built bioweapon developed to damage and kill us. The Covid "vaccine" injections are a second attack. The "elites" continue to conceal treatments that would have halted the pandemic. See Part 3, The Covid and Vax Disasters.
- Promoting "transgender" (TG) behavior using drugs and surgery turns this improbable condition into a lifelong agony rather than a temporary adolescent rebellion. The medicines kill fertility, suppress orgasms, and destroy

normal development. Forty percent of transgenders attempt suicide. The psychopaths are sponsoring marketing claiming that TGs are cousins of our gays and lesbians (reference HERE). But most gays and lesbians know this is a lie and refuse to be identified with it. See Part 7.

- Psychopaths are grooming pedophilia by bringing drag queens into elementary schools. The World Economic Forum argues that laws against pedophilia "violate human rights."
- They are embezzling our money using money printing. It is the most massive financial crime in history, and their motive is economic collapse. See the interview with Edward Dowd in Part 11.
- They are inciting war.
- They have thrown open our borders to foreign predators. This encourages human trafficking and the onslaught of devastating narcotics.
- For decades, psychopaths have promoted harmful prescription drugs that destroy health and cause violence, suicide, and insanity. Psych drugs are the worst, but there are many others. See *Butchered by "Healthcare"* and Parts 3 through 8.
- They pay incentives to hospitals for the mistreatment and killing Covid patients. See Part 4, Hospitals Have Become Contract Killers.
- Racism and social strife are promoted with ANTIFA, Black Lives Matter, the election of false prosecutors, and the "defund the police"

propaganda. See the Reality Inversion chapter in Part 2.

- One of the conspirator's goals is to forbid gun carry by private citizens. This 2nd Amendment right promotes security and combats crime. See the guns chapter in Part 11, Lawyers, Guns, and Money.
- The psychopaths claim "carbon is bad for the earth" and global warming will kill us all. These theories are precisely the opposite of the truth and have become a false religion. These lies are used to decrease energy use and, therefore, worldwide food production, with the ultimate goal of starving "carbon-based life forms"— people. Even if these theories were true, nuclear energy could safely and opulently support our food and water production. It is carbon neutral and would be cheap at scale, but they are suppressing it. See Part 9, Climatology.

They call this the "Great Reset." The plan is to destroy our rule of law, social fabric, and the United States itself. Their goal is an economic crash and then a totalitarian government.

Free countries are the most creative and productive, so not even psychopaths can explain how the Chinese system or a financial collapse would make them wealthier. But the whole thing makes sense to them because their primary goal is not money. They want to torture, destroy, and control. Since they are sadists, they enjoy the process.

Psychopaths use a strategy called "gaslighting" (Part 2). This is lying, terrorizing, and intimidating to alter their victims' perceived reality. Ordinary people who cannot imagine basing their lives on falsehoods have trouble understanding what is happening.

The "conspiracy theory" phrase is being used to convince some of our best thinkers to dismiss current reality as improbable (Part 2). Many have been hoodwinked into exhaustive, repeated attempts to explain how it all could have happened. The academic controversies they debate are trivial—they are splitting hairs when they should be trying to figure out how to put the criminals down. The actual battle is against lies and censors.

To fathom today's reality, consider the creatures who surrounded Hitler. The most skilled members of this species are rarely captured and seldom examined forensically. The Nuremberg Trial defendants were an exception. Although these animals imitated human behavior, they had no morals, feelings, or genuine relationships. The key to understanding today's events is to realize that thousands of these brutes now walk among us. Due to unprecedented disparities of wealth and power, they may be gaining the upper hand.

Lower-functioning psychopaths are similar structurally but possess less guile and intelligence. Since they have more trouble concealing their intentions and behavior, they are sometimes captured, imprisoned, and studied. They occasionally get herded where they belong—into the justice system's insect-killing jar. The insights from collecting these specimens provide inferences about their cousins, the corporate and political leaders. Although these deviants have been studied and observed, our knowledge about them is imperfect.

Robert Hare compiled the Psychopath Test. Its diagnostic value is weak, but true sociopaths live on across a bright line. Those around them—the variants—have a spectrum of the following traits.

- Glibness/superficial charm
- Grandiose sense of self-worth
- Pathological lying
- Conning/manipulative
- Lack of remorse or guilt
- Shallow affect
- Callous/lack of empathy
- Failure to accept responsibility for own actions
- Need for stimulation/proneness to boredom
- Parasitic lifestyle
- Poor behavioral controls
- Promiscuous sexual behavior (Example: Epstein and associates' pedophilia.)
- Lack of realistic, long-term goals
- Impulsivity
- Irresponsibility
- Juvenile delinquency
- Early behavior problems
- Revocation of conditional release (violation of the terms of release from a psych facility, typically with reincarceration)
- Criminal versatility
- Many short-term marital relationships

The titles of three popular books describe these monsters well: *Snakes in Suits* (2006, Paul Babiak and Robert D. Hare), *Without Conscience* (1993, Robert Hare), and *The Mask of Sanity* (1941, Hervey M. Cleckley). *Political Ponerology* (1984) by Andrzej Łobaczewski is the most comprehensive source. He says that psychopaths, conspiring in networks, have significant political and economic power. Their banality and seeming normalcy defy easy identification even by experts.

Łobaczewski writes, "[Sociopaths] learn to recognize each other in a crowd... sometimes in childhood. They become conscious of being different from the people surrounding them." He says that they view the rest of us as almost another species.

They know truth, honor, and decency but do not think these apply to them. They cheat, break promises, and revile the non-psychopaths. They use fear, lies, and concealment as weapons. They covet possessions and power and feel they have the right to them because they can take them. They plagiarize, swindle, and extort. The fruits obtained this way are sweeter for them than those earned through honest labor.

These degenerates have no conscience, do not feel others' pain, and use their traits to reap benefits and pull strings. They learn that their personalities traumatize others and use this to their advantage. Those who know nothing about them are the most easily deceived and manipulated.

When government leaders and business CEOs are psychopaths, their immorality infects those around them. Conscienceless people create an environment where greed, deception, and even violence become the norm. Weaker individuals model them to survive. Although these followers may not be not "genetic" or total psychopaths, they turn into "effective" psychopaths.

Robert D. Hare describes them, "Psychopaths have a narcissistic and grossly inflated view of their self-worth and importance, a truly astounding egocentricity and sense of entitlement, and see themselves as the center of the universe, as superior beings who are justified in living according to their own rules."

Full psychopaths use their knowledge of ordinary people's sensitivities to manipulate them. They may fake empathy yet remain aloof and calculating. Some use tears or shouting to whiplash their victims' emotions.

We do not know their thoughts, but their actions reveal them. Incessant lying, or a stark mismatch between words and actions, is the easiest way to spot them. It is a successful strategy because most of us have trouble believing that anyone does this routinely. Normal people may struggle with their mental health as they deal with this.

The central mystery is how these vermin could have gained so much control. Łobaczewski believes "essential," or total psychopaths, are about 1% of the population. When other related syndromes are considered, the core group might be about 6 percent. He believed that the most pathological personalities are the most likely to develop positions of power.

The next tier of about 12 percent is more healthy but has been damaged by long-term exposure to the leaders. Working together, these groups conspire to subdue and control the rest of the population. The masses can be led to believe almost any far-fetched idea by using media control. Ordinary people mostly follow whoever seems to be in charge.

Psychopathic regimes find compliant scientists, support their academic degrees and achievements, and advance them into leadership. These obliging tools know their work is monitored for proper ideology and that their handlers would destroy them if they stepped out of line. See RFK Jr.'s book *The Real Anthony Fauci* for many examples.

These degenerates conceal themselves using politics

and ideology. Left, right, center, socialist, democratic, communist, Democrat, and Republican are meaningless deceptions to them. When all political parties serve the same monsters, it erodes social structures and has cancerous effects on nations. Only a few people understand this and speak out.

Since legal and political systems developed partly under the influence of psychopaths, these structures may be insufficient to control them. Many observers believe that substantial secret governments have always existed, even when the recognized system is virtuous. For example, the Warren Commission asked us to believe the improbable story that a second lone actor immediately assassinated JFK's killer. The records of this event are still being concealed:

> One of the new documents related to a still-classified covert operation — still classified nearly 60 years later — that had been approved by senior CIA officials three months before Kennedy's death, suggesting the agency employed Kennedy's assassin Lee Harvey Oswald for intelligence purposes just weeks before the shooting.
>
> In other words, Oswald worked for the CIA — AT LEAST up to three weeks before the killing.

The CIA has never acknowledged its link to Oswald before, not at the time or in all the decades after, not during Democrat nor Republican administrations. You would think they might have mentioned that tiny fact if they had nothing to hide. They might have useful intel on Oswald and his relationships in their CIA employee files, information that might have helped at the time.

John F. Kennedy was on the point of exposing some of

this, as he expressed in THIS speech. It is likely the reason he was murdered.

Here are what check psychopaths

- A bigger psychopath
- Fear of prosecution and punishment
- Exposure and ostracism
- The absolute refusal to submit to their control regardless of the consequences
- Death

How can anyone say no? Millions took to the streets before the invasion of Iraq, but it did not matter because the leaders did not care. They controlled the military and the media, which was used to paint dissenters as traitors. This happened recently to those who did not consent to the jab or comply with the lockdowns.

If every normal person refused to lift a hand to further these agendas, the system would grind to a halt. But that can only happen when everyone is miserable enough that the pain psychopaths can inflict pales compared to current conditions. It might also occur when there is general knowledge about the world being created for our children.

We must learn to spot psychopaths, speak up, and never be dominated. We must refuse to be conned or used. Giving in to anything they suggest is a mistake, for it emboldens them.

Today's criminals realize they have committed multiple capital crimes. They also know they are a tiny minority. Let us hope that enough remains of our will, our courts, and our tattered constitution to save us.

For a bibliography and more, see the TMI (too

much information) about Psychopaths, Chapter 55 in Part 13.

The core reference for this chapter is Silvia Cattori's 2008 review of *Political Ponerology* HERE. This book is the most complete source about psychopaths.

Research and insight credit for this article: my collaborator Sherman (hat tip to the 1960s Rocky and Bullwinkle Show for his pseudonym).

Chapter 3
Interview With a Psychopath Expert

What makes psychopaths different from all others is the remarkable ease with which they lie, the pervasiveness of their deception, and the callousness with which they carry it out.

> — Robert D. Hare, *Without Conscience: The Disturbing World of the Psychopaths Among Us*

Although Harrison Koehli is fascinated with psychopaths, he is a "normie" like the rest of us. He spent eight months editing the most comprehensive book about them, *Political Ponerology*. Since this is a difficult read, I scanned the popular books first. His substack blog and podcast is https://ponerology.substack.com. Warning: it is technical.

During our interview, Harrison helped me understand the following ideas and others:

- How countries can gradually become dominated by networks of psychopaths to become "pathocracies."
- How to recognize them.
- How they are parasites and contribute little or nothing of productive value.
- How they sadistically enjoy other people's pain and suffering.

SUBSTACK LINK

Chapter 4
The Final Solution, Then and Now, by Holocaust Survivor Vira Sharav

If only we had stood together against the common threat, we could easily have defeated it. So, why didn't we? ... We didn't love freedom enough ... we hurried to submit. We submitted with pleasure! ... We purely and simply deserved everything that happened afterward.

— Alexander Solzhenitsyn

Vera Sharav is a Holocaust survivor. She calls herself a public advocate for human rights and is founder and president of the Alliance for Human Research Protection (AHRP.org). This is her August 20, 2022, speech at Nuremberg from the Children's Health Defense website. She says that the Holocaust developed in a way that was uncannily similar to today. Phrases such as "useless eaters" are being reused.

She began, "In 1941, I was 3 1/2 when my family was forced from our home in Romania & deported to Ukraine. We were herded into a concentration camp – essentially left to starve. Death was ever-present. My father died of typhus when I was five."

The original video is HERE. I also interviewed Vera on a recent podcast HERE.

SUBSTACK LINK

Chapter 5
Diversion: TMI About Yoho

If you do this work, expect trouble.

— Julius Newman, a prominent cosmetic
surgeon

I am not so brave. The reason I am uncensored is because I resigned my medical license. This seemed like a loss at the time, but it preserved my integrity and allowed me to write freely. I had a fantastic career and was initially sad to end it, but I was happy that I still had a small part of my life left to research and write full-time.

SUBSTACK LINK

I attended Oberlin College and did medical training at major centers, including Dartmouth, Case Western, and the University of Southern California. I had idealistic mentors, but since I am unconventional, few bonded with me, and my path was lonely.

I was a late developer and always considered medicine secondary to my other interests. I once told my wife and kids—half tongue in cheek—that my climbing career overshadowed all the rest. Despite this tepid commitment, even in elite physicians' company, I was bright enough to backstroke through the academics. A friend once told me that I was a "quirky genius." But this ambiguous compliment was a one-off—no one else before or since has been so kind. And my buddy had a massive stroke after the Covid vax, so there is no proof that he ever said it.

My medical career was boring compared to climbing.

I climbed Yosemite's El Capitan in a day.

I broke my foot during a forty-foot swinging fall on
another trip.

A dear friend in front of the East Face of El Capitan.

I do not know what I was thinking in those days. I
ruptured my biceps, broke my foot in a long fall (it still talks
to me), and had two knee surgeries after ripping my quadri-

26

ceps muscle off one kneecap. The rescuers needed a heli-copter to pick me up for that one. Another time, I remember hooking a front tooth over a handhold while frantically trying not to fall. I broke it in half when I slipped. And I recently had both shoulders replaced.

Residency required more time and energy. I wrote an account of one period in *Butchered by 'Healthcare:"*

> I tried to become a dermatologist once. These specialists stay cleverly in their own world, avoid dealing with serious problems, and make a lot of money without losing sleep. It seemed like a masterful concept. I was an annoying young man, but through family connections and somehow conjuring a fragile veneer of charm, I got accepted into one of their most selective training programs.

I thought this feat qualified me for the dermatologic life-style and wanted to spend my weekends hiking the Appalachian Trail. My mentors, however, thought I should spend 70 hours a week learning about skin disease. After a year, they exposed me as a poseur and kicked me out.

I viewed it as a personal failure, but I smelled something fishy the whole time. I was too close to see clearly and had plenty of problems, so I could not put my finger on it. Like the dermatologists trying to teach me, I did not know their history. (Learn more about them in the Butchered ebook, $3.)

I finished training and then board-certified in Emer-gency Medicine. It seemed like the right match for me. I could take time off, and I developed skills I thought I could use on international climbing expeditions. But both of these plans were absurd fantasies that never worked out.

I learned that hospital emergency rooms were political war zones and that night shifts damaged my health. Since my skills were related to family practice, I switched to that after a few years. But generalists make less money than specialists, and my pay never seemed like enough. So, for over a decade, I attended hands-on training seminars every month and acquired many plastic surgery skills.

I eventually developed a high-volume cosmetic surgery practice and met my first true mentors and colleagues. Since I had not spent the usual years in hospital surgical residencies, I limited my practice to less complex procedures. But cosmetic surgery complications are inevitable, and in California, lawsuits are part of the game.

(Continued at the end of Part 2)

Part Two

Gaslighting Has Nothing to do With Propane

Chapter 6
History and Techniques

If you're part of a poker game and don't know who the patsy is, it's you.

— Anon

"Gaslighting" is Merriam-Webster's word of the year. CBS News reported:
"Lookups for the word on Merriam-Webster.com increased 1,740% in 2022 over the year before. But something else happened. There wasn't a single event that drove significant spikes in the curiosity, as it usually goes with the chosen word of the year. The gaslighting was pervasive..."

Merriam-Webster's top definition for gaslighting is the psychological manipulation of a person, usually over an extended period of time, that "causes the victim to question the validity of their own thoughts, perception of reality, or memories and typically leads to confusion, loss of confidence and self-esteem, uncertainty of one's emotional or mental stability, and a dependency on the perpetrator."

CJ Hopkins, one of my top sources, describes what has happened:

In a little over two and a half years, our collective "reality" has been radically revised. Our societies have been radically restructured. Millions (probably billions) of people have been systematically conditioned to believe a variety of patently ridiculous assertions, assertions based on absolutely nothing, repeatedly disproved by widely available evidence, but which have nevertheless attained the status of facts. An entire fictitious history has been written based on those baseless and ridiculous assertions. It will not be unwritten easily or quickly...

One of the most basic and effective techniques that cults, totalitarian systems, and individuals with fascistic personalities use to disorient and control people's minds is "gaslighting." ...

The main goal of gaslighting is to confuse, coerce, and emotionally manipulate your victim into abandoning their own perception of reality and accepting whatever new "reality" you impose on them. Ultimately, you want to completely destroy their ability to trust their own perception, emotions, reasoning, and memory of historical events, and render them utterly dependent on you to tell them what is real and what "really" happened, and so on, and how they should be feeling about it.

Anyone who has ever experienced gaslighting in the context of an abusive relationship, or a cult, or a totalitarian system, or who has worked in a battered women's shelter, can tell you how powerful and destructive it is. In the most extreme cases, the victims of gaslighting are entirely stripped of their sense of self and surrender their individual autonomy completely. Among the best-known and most dramatic exam-

ples are the Patty Hearst case, Jim Jones's People's Temple, the Manson family, and various other cults, but, the truth is, gaslighting happens every day, out of the spotlight of the media, in countless personal and professional relationships.

Since the Spring of 2020, we have been subjected to official gaslighting on an unprecedented scale. In a sense, the "Apocalyptic Pandemic" PSYOP has been one big extended gaslighting campaign (comprising countless individual instances of gaslighting) inflicted on the masses throughout the world...

In order to effectively gaslight someone, you have be in a position of authority or wield some other form of power over them. They have to need something vital from you (i.e., sustenance, safety, financial security, community, career advancement, or just love). You can't walk up to some random stranger on the street and start gaslighting them. They will laugh in your face.

The reason the New Normal authorities have been able to gaslight the masses so effectively is that most of the masses do need something from them ... a job, food, shelter, money, security, status, their friends, a relationship, or whatever it is they're not willing to risk by challenging those in power and their lies. Gaslighters, cultists, and power freaks, generally, know this. It is what they depend on, your unwillingness to live without whatever it is. They zero in on it and threaten you with the loss of it (sometimes consciously, sometimes just intuitively).

Gaslighting won't work if you are willing to give up whatever the gaslighter is threatening to take from you (or stop giving you, as the case may be), but you have to be willing to actually lose it, because you will be punished for defending yourself, for not surrendering your autonomy and integrity, and conforming to the "reality" of the cult, or the abusive relationship, or the totalitarian system.

Government, tech companies, and mainstream and social media are telling lies, flip-flopping, and exaggerating to make us anxious, intimidate us, and lure us away from reality. We are forced to assume that talking heads are lying if their mouths are moving. We also know that declaring something a "conspiracy theory" or "misinformation" means it is likely true. We recognize that Google searches are tightly controlled. They lose power if we understand all this and can ignore it all.

(Image originally appeared HERE.)

* * *

Our government has a long history of behavior like this. Here are some key events:

- In 1843, the first advertising agency in the US was founded.
- In 1917, President Wilson formed the Committee on Public Information. This was

designed to goad the US public into entering the war in Europe ("German soldiers skewering Belgian babies on bayonets!!")

- In 1942, President Roosevelt created the Office of War Information (OWI) and the Office of Strategic Services (OSS).
- In 1945, President Truman transferred propaganda operations to the Department of State.
- In 1947, President Truman replaced the OSS with the Central Intelligence Agency (CIA).
- In 1947, (one month later) President Truman signed The National Security Act creating the National Security Council. Many consider this the birth of "the deep state" or "the shadow government."
- In 1948, the Smith-Mundt Act authorized the State Department to propagandize foreign countries as a form of public diplomacy but forbade doing so within the US.
- *In 2012, the Smith-Mundt Modernization Act, signed by President Obama, eliminated the prohibition on inside-the-US propaganda. It permitted the federal government to lie to us.*

On July 19, 2010, the Washington Post reported about the US "security" state:

Some 1,271 government organizations and 1,931 private companies work on programs related to counterterrorism, homeland security, and intelligence in about 10,000 locations across the United States. An estimated 854,000 people, nearly 1 ½ times as many people as live in Washington, D.C., hold top-secret security clearances. In Washington and the surrounding area, 33 building complexes for top-secret intelligence work are under construction or have been built since September 2001. Together they occupy the equivalent of almost three Pentagons or 22 U.S. Capitol buildings...

The academics are piling on by studying which government propaganda techniques work best. Yale, for example, in December 2021, published Persuasive messaging to increase COVID-19 vaccine uptake intentions in *Vaccine*. The authors claimed no conflicts of interest as if they funded the massive study themselves.

We are paying these jackals to spy on us (illegal) and lie to us (now legal). How do they pull it off? Their brainwashing methods include repetition, fear-mongering, censoring news, and using celebrities. Here are others that you may recognize from recent history:

- *Conspiracy Theory.* Calling something a 'conspiracy theory' switches off many people's interest. After John Kennedy's assassination, the CIA used this to discredit the evidence that they murdered him. This rhetoric has been effective again and again.
- *Additional Evidence Required.* But the public never hears the challenges because of censorship. This has been used many times during the Covid operation.
- *Appeal to Authority.* For example, Fauci has famously equated himself with "the Science."

- *Name Calling and Ridicule.* Schoolyard stuff, yes, but it will drive away a certain percentage of readers who cannot handle unpleasantness.
- *Bandwagon.* Claiming "people who care about others are all getting vaccinated."
- *Unwarranted Extrapolation.* "If you do not get vaccinated, this pandemic will continue for years."
- *Loaded Questions.* Have you stopped beating your wife? "Black Lives Matter, Science is Real, and No Human is Illegal" were all used recently. In normal times, the intersection of these very distinct matters would have been dismissed as a childish ploy. But during Covid, it worked. The accused has nothing to say lest they seem guilty.
- *Become Indignant.* "How dare you say that masks are not effective."
- *The Straw Man.* Focus on the weakest element of the opposition's claims and address only that element, or create a similar-seeming body of information that is designed to be attackable
- *Concoct Motives.* Invent hidden agendas to apply to your opponent.
- *Call for a Special Investigation.* An expensive form of dawdling masquerading as a response.
- *Glittering Generalities.* The opposite of Name Calling. Casting a halo of goodness over a favored person, group, or behavior.
- *Plain Folks.* Portraying notable persons of extreme privilege as just like you and me, e.g., Bill Clinton eating at Mcdonalds'.

- *Frame as Rumor.* The story comes from the wrong side of the tracks. "Another internet rumor."
- *Disingenuous Confession.* Select a trivial element of the opponent's complaint, confess "unfortunate mistakes were made," and so on. These crocodile tears gain goodwill from the naïve.
- *It's Complicated.* The burdens of complexity make for an imperfect world; indeed, a reasonable person would understand.
- *Demand Perfection.* The opponent must solve and explain every aspect of the undesirable program or event. Otherwise, they are just whining and shooting from the hip.
- *Ignore the Proof Presented.* It sounds like it would not work very well, but tragically it does. This has happened every month since March 2020.
- *Teamwork.* TV, print, celebrity, scientist, and law enforcement agree on the significant issue. This costs a lot of money and is ideal for a fascist government, which is an amalgam of state and corporate interests.
- For more, see the Supplement at the end of this chapter.

SUBSTACK LINK

The government, tech companies, and academics are feeding us these lies in a power play. Disorienting and intimidating using the Covid story is just their start. If we give up our peace of mind to the global psychopaths, they can herd us in any direction and fleece us. They are using this strategy out of weakness, not strength, however—if they could, they would march us around at gunpoint.

These "psy-ops" (psychological operations) are designed to change our view of reality. As they feed us lies about carbon excess, incessant nonsense about transgenders, and even try to normalize pedophilia, we are the well-known frog in the lukewarm cooking pot heading toward a boil. The news, the CDC, the FDA, the CIA, and other agencies coordinate the deceptions.

Edward Snowden weighs in about the CIA HERE:

> From the year it was established, Presidents and their cadres have regularly directed the CIA to go beyond the law for reasons that cannot be justified, and therefore must be concealed—classified. The primary result of the classification system is not an increase in national security, but a decrease in transparency. Without meaningful transparency, there is no accountability, and without accountability, there is no learning.

Think back five years. Would you have thought it normal to have a cotton swab shoved up your nose when you feel fine—to see if you are sick? We must fight to ensure that this absurdity and many others are never viewed as normal.

In *Man's Search for Meaning*, Viktor Frankl wrote, "Everything can be taken from a man but one thing: the last of the human freedoms—to choose one's attitude in any given set of circumstances, to choose one's own way." He was in a concentration camp and helpless, but our situation is entirely different. We have many actions that we can take.

General awareness of the evil deeds is finally percolating through our society. Criminal prosecutions or civil lawsuits are starting or pending, and hundreds of offenders are guilty of horrific crimes. We have the power to punish them, and we must seize it. Through it all, we must maintain equanimity, learn what is true, and understand that nearly all we hear from the propaganda machine is fear porn that must be ignored. We must never let gangsters psych us out.

Sources

- My bro Sherman contributed most of this essay's content.
- *The Mighty Wurlitzer: How the CIA Played America Paperback, by Hugh Wilford.* This explains how many of the military information warriors of WW2 migrated to Madison Avenue and the secret federal agencies after the war.
- *Presstitutes Embedded in the Pay of the CIA: A Confession from the Profession by Dr. Udo Ulfkotte.* A German journalist exposed the present-day workings of the CIA in its ongoing

efforts to control information in the US and the world.

Supplement: more techniques.

- *Never Show Anger*. Let the opponent get angry. Your constant calm implies the opponent doesn't understand proper social behavior.
- *Framing*. Many things are reported in the news, but few are explained. Events seem random and surprising, never resulting from evil forces or hidden influencers.
- *Guilt by Association*. Associate the opponent with an already disliked group. E.g., "Mr. Complainer, reading from the white supremacist playbook, says that..."
- *Least of Evils*. The criticized act/program can be compared to worse alternatives, and the worse, the better.
- *Virtue Words*. For example, Biden says Trump's MAGA hordes threaten DEMOCRACY.
- *Humor*. For example, political cartoons imply that if an issue can be made fun of, it is under control, and only a Nervous Nellie would truly fret about it.
- *Pure Motives*. As the governors of our states persisted in destroying small businesses during lockdowns, they reminded us they were "acting out of an abundance of caution."
- *Selective Omission*. The propagandist cherry-picks his facts and avoids the embarrassing bits.

- *Misquote to Condemn.* Usually involves abridging a statement and taking it out of context.
- *False Dichotomy.* Two choices are offered when others are viable. Our present reality is built on this deception: Republican/Democrat, pro-vax/anti-vax, CNN/Fox.
- *Slippery Slope.* The propagandist claims non-compliance is disaster.
- *Anonymous Authority.* "Scientists have found... Doctors have warned... Reliable authorities predict..."
- *Attack the Authority.* For Covid, "Dr. So-and-So is a trauma surgeon, not an infectious disease specialist."
- *Style Over Substance. The Atlantic. The New Yorker.* This is expensive and thus ideal for corporate-government fascism.
- *Strategic Labeling.* Positive: the healthy economy and strong national security. Negative: leftist guerillas, civil disturbance, controversial claim.
- *Slighting of Content.* For elections: who was nominated, how they are polling, how their party is polling without discussing the issues.
- *Blame Game.* Most people want to blame someone, so there is low resistance to accepting a scapegoat.
- *Create a Bigger Distraction.* When all else fails.

Chapter 7
Slaves Have Been Forced to Wear Masks Throughout History

Mandated masking is gaslighting on steroids. Masks say we will submit to any absurd lie put before us by the psychopaths. Masks say we are broken.

— Contributor EC

R oberto Strongman wrote THIS brilliant article, published on November 4, 2021, and I condensed and abridged it with permission. Any mistakes or misinterpretations are mine.

Every medical authority, including Fauci, has known from the start that masks neither prevent the spread nor protect against viruses. Masking healthy people has no rational basis—over 200 studies refute its efficacy. And although masking surgeons keeps blood off the doctors, *Cochrane Reviews* concludes, "there is no clear evidence that wearing disposable face masks affects the likelihood of wound infections developing after surgery."

But by now, many people are so traumatized that they are afraid to show their faces. They have been intimidated into cowardly obedience signaling, and the masks are being used to express compliance.

Escrava Anastácia (Wikimedia Commons)

Anti-lockdown protester in Melbourne, Australia.
Photo credit: YouTube video posted by 10 News
First, September 5, 2020.

Escrava Anastácia is a Brazilian folk saint. She has a shrine in the Church of Our Lady of the Rosary of Black People in Salvador da Bahia, and many black Brazilian

Catholics venerate her. But she has never been acknowledged or canonized by the Roman Catholic Church.

A slave owner punished, silenced, and likely raped Anastácia. In some versions of the story, the plantation's mistress muzzled Anastásia to save herself from the public shame of her husband's infidelity. In others, her muzzling was to punish her for her leadership in a slave revolt. A third story was that she aided a runaway slave. Her muzzling was a deterrent to others.

SUBSTACK LINK

Anastásia's legend was that she could perform miracles even while muzzled. She was said to heal her oppressors. Her compassion towards her persecutors and her possible mixed-race background were thought by many to be a hopeful sign of racial reconciliation in Brazil.

She died of starvation or possibly tetanus from the metal rusting in her mouth. Her ghost is seen at anti-lockdown rallies, and her memory shows that the current medical tyranny is enslavement.

Guantánamo prisoners forced to wear masks. Image
credit: AP Photo/Brennan Llinsley.

Some of today's psychologists are captives of the mask propaganda. Susan Michie, for example, claims we will be wearing masks forever (Stone 2021).

Face masks are slave symbols:

- Masking imposes control and breaks down psyches, dignity, and integrity.
- They are symbols of submission, forced compliance, and arbitrary rules.
- They make it harder to breathe. This makes people susceptible to brainwashing.
- Face masks are involved in bondage and sadomasochism. This is a master-slave dynamic.
- Masks are a feature of prisons and torture. Examples include the dehumanizing hoods on the Abu Ghraib prison victims and the mouth covers at Guantánamo.
- Masking is a nameless, enforced uniformity that erases individual personhood.

Cassandra's Memo

- Masks are theatrical. They conceal our identities, rendering us alien to others and ourselves.
- Masks are a forced socialization into the "new normal." The more we accept this enslavement ritual, the harder it will be to regain our independence.
- The masks are a state insignia. They are a visible display of allegiance to the system of medicalizing control. They are related to the red neckerchiefs of the Chinese communist pioneer youth movement, which were a public profession of loyalty to the party and Mao, the supreme leader. His idea of "right thinking" has found new life in today's America.
- The absence of facial expressions with masking inhibits the non-verbal communication necessary for social organization that might lead to revolt.
- Masks reduce communication, and their usage is isolating. Social distancing has similar effects.
- Animals are trained with muzzles. When used on people, they are symbols of dehumanization.
- Masks are just a few steps away from shots, vaccine passports, and implantable monitoring devices.
- Every mask is a billboard for fear and a state of emergency. We are being subjugated to scaremongering, which is eroding our civil liberties.
- Masks make your neighbor a nameless disease vector instead of a friend and ally. Masks divide and conquer.

A representation of a slave at work cruelly accoutred, with a Head-frame and Mouth-piece to prevent his eating—with Boots and Spurs round his legs, and half a hundred weight chained to his body to prevent his absconding.

Photo credit: Library Company of Philadelphia.

Anastásia's image is a powerful religious spectacle. Can her memory overcome the Covidian cult? For members of the freedom movement who are spiritual, our visions of Anastásia give us faith.

Balls, chains, and shackles were iron, but in our technological age, the bonds are fragile symbols such as paper masks. Yet they are potentially more brutal and confining than the old ones.

Those who cannot or refuse to see masks and the rest of our era's indignities as enslavement are hypnotized. If they acknowledge what is happening, they lose face, which is embarrassing and painful.

Many people on both sides of the Atlantic who lived in

the preindustrial and even Civil War times believed slavery was natural. Today, people are brainwashed into near slavery by accepting endless, medicalized confinements and inconveniences through various control techniques.

How often have we heard the "new normies" say the purpose of curtailing our civil liberties is the excesses of mass gatherings and the so-called super-spreader events? They have been indoctrinated to believe we have brought the situation on ourselves by not cooperating. Guilt is weaponized, "science" is a religion, and we supposedly deserve the lockdowns.

The Spanish word "bozal" has two meanings: a muzzle and a newly arrived slave born in Africa. The muzzle devices were used on bozal slaves who had memories of freedom from their homeland and were the most likely to lead rebellions.

The mask symbolizes enslavement, and Anastásia's message is for us all.

Roberto Strongman is an Associate Professor in the Department of Black Studies at the University of California, Santa Barbara. He received his Ph.D. in Literature from the University of California, San Diego, in 2003. Dr. Strongman's interdisciplinary approach encompasses the fields of religion, history, and sexuality to further his main area of research and teaching: Comparative Caribbean Cultural Studies (from his website).

Roberto is a modern social science academic, so he writes using their problematic style. He kindly permitted me to rewrite his valuable contribution in more straightforward prose.

Chapter 8
Ignore Reality Inversion

Everything You Believe is Wrong

— Title of Matt Brigg's 2021 book

W e should tattoo this on our wrists, for if we are not careful, we will waste our lives analyzing gaslighting. We may never regain the emotional energy we lose.

THE BLACK LIVES MATTER movement is a case in point. They claim white policemen are murdering Black Americans wholesale. The media reports make this seem plausible.

But police are continuously monitored by video cameras worn on their bodies, and additional video surveillance is everywhere. Incidents of any kind are analyzed, and these sources frequently release footage that is picked up by platforms such as YouTube's Active Self-

Protection (ASP). If you watch this, you will see how difficult police work is and, as a bonus, learn how to prevent violent crime. Be careful—this channel is addictive.

Black men are not being shot at a higher level than white men, and the statistics prove it. Black-on-black crime is well known to be a far bigger problem, and in some areas, residents hide in bathtubs when the shooting starts. This deserves serious attention and not propaganda. Effective ideas—such as more police, preferably from the area—are dismissed, and anti-police BLM propaganda is used to invert the issue.

Like so many of the lies we deal with, the Black Lives Matter drivel is hyped by groups trying to use internal dissent to destroy our country. The numbers do not bear out "murder by police."

SUBSTACK LINK

* * *

INVERSION AFTER INVERSION

Remember the "horse drug campaign" about ivermectin? This familiar lie was the claim by the FDA and CDC that ivermectin and hydroxychloroquine did not help

Covid. But early use of these medications, along with zinc and vitamin D, would have saved more than three-quarters of those who died. Contrast these messages:

> 2015: "Ivermectin May Fight Malaria... Older drugs, like many older people, are a source rich in treasures."
> 2021: "You are not a horse." The FDA tells Americans to stop taking 'dewormer' for Covid.

The "Emergency Use Authorization" invoked to allow the "vaccine" rollout is permitted only when no other treatment works. If these drugs were acknowledged effective, the vaccine could not have been authorized, and the people who died from the jab would be alive today.

Pfizers' imitation ("pfizermectin"), Paxlovid, is toxic and associated with rebound Covid infection in six to ten percent of patients. It costs $529 for a five-day treatment course.

LIE AFTER LIE

Pfizer's Covid vax kills pregnancies, and they covered it up. (From *The Expose*)

> A 'Freedom of Information' request alongside an in-depth dive into the only pregnancy/fertility study performed on the Pfizer Covid-19 injection has revealed that Medicine Regulators and Pfizer chose to publicly cover up alarming abnormalities of the developing fetus and falsely downgraded the actual risk of Covid-19 vaccination during pregnancy by suppressing documented findings of the clinical data.

These decisions led medical professionals, who are far too trusting of Medicine Regulators, to wrongly inform pregnant women that the Covid-19 injections are perfectly safe during pregnancy, leading to many pregnant women feeling pressured to get vaccinated.

This fraud and deception have caused at least 4,113 foetal deaths due to Covid-19 vaccination in the USA alone, and a further study shows Covid-19 vaccination increases the risk of suffering a miscarriage by at least 1,517%.

AND ABSURDITY AFTER ABSURDITY

"I got a stroke right after the jab."
"Must have been that climate change."

Social media has photographs of a huge sign hanging from a bridge saying, "NEED AN ABORTION? TRY THE COVID VACCINE." Unfortunately, this is anything but absurd.

The goal of this kind of propaganda – or disinformation – campaign is to simply overwhelm the reader, the listener, the viewer, until he or she surrenders to the message, concedes its validity, and, crucially, follows its mandates... As one after another individual falls into compliance, group-think forms, and resisters are soon conquered by peer pressure. As anyone knows, standing against a crowd is not only frightening but requires a kind of fortitude that few possess... (unknown source)

* * *

Robert Yoho, MD (ret)

Turning off mainstream media is a survival skill. Guard your thoughts and be careful whom you trust.

— A contributor

Chapter 9
Mercola: Fake Fact Checking and Ruining the Wayback Machine

The Wayback Machine Internet Archive is all that prevents censors from rewriting our history, but it is in jeopardy.

— Dr. Mercola

By Joseph Mercola, February 09, 2022. Voice performance by Robert Yoho. This subject is important and worth a quick scan. I subscribe to daily posts at Mercola.com.

SUBSTACK LINK

STORY AT-A-GLANCE

Investigative journalist Sharyl Attkisson explains how virtually everything you see and hear online has been co-opted or taken over to serve another agenda.

Fact-checking is one part of the campaign to control what you see online, and therefore what you think and how you perceive reality

Instead of real journalists and reporters, the media is infiltrated with propagandists who dictate what's "fake news" and what's not

The public is being manipulated to want their information censored by third-party "fact"-checkers, which were introduced as a tool to confuse and control the public further

"Conspiracy theory," "misinformation," "debunked," "quackery," "fact-checked," "content moderation," and "antivaccine" are examples of terms that are being used as propaganda tools; they are badges of fraud

Those who rely solely on the internet for their information are being controlled. You can fight back by doing your own research and trusting your common sense

Before 2015 or 2016, information was freely available online with little interference. But since then, propagandists have infiltrated the internet. Working with Big Tech and government, they began to control information. "Fact-checking" is a once-obscure term that has since gone mainstream. This is one part of the campaign to control what you see online, and therefore what you believe.

Speaking with Jan Jekielek, The *Epoch Times* senior editor and host of the show "American Thought Leaders," investigative journalist Sharyl Attkisson explains how almost everything you see and hear online has been taken over to serve an agenda:1 "One has to understand that nearly every mode of information has been co-opted. Fact checks are no different. They have been either captured or created to distribute narratives and propaganda." Your common sense will help you decipher what is true.

Information is being controlled. Several key online sources are heavily manipulated. These include Wikipedia, Snopes, most "fact" checkers, and HealthFeedback.org. This last is a fake-science group used by Facebook and other Big Tech companies to make real science seem false.

Fact-checkers are often referred to as scientists, but this is propaganda. And while there have always been efforts to shape media information, news reporters formerly would try to get both sides of the story.

But beginning in the early 2000s, efforts were started to prevent some information from being reported. Pharmaceutical companies hired global PR firms to do this. These firms also partnered with government.

Suppressing and censoring information took off in 2015 to 2016, when Donald Trump was perceived to be a unique threat by both Democrats and Republicans. Since then, these techniques have become commonplace.

After he won the election, a campaign was organized that exploited the already frenzied media. The result was today's crazy information landscape. Journalists no longer try to uncover the truth. Instead, they parrot whatever establishment scientists or politicians want them to say.

The new media is infiltrated with propagandists who

dictate what's "fake news" and what's not. Many believe that fake news is a product of Trump, but Big Tech created a lobbying campaign of propagandists. Fact-checking and censoring were born.

The term "fake news" was popularized after Trump was elected, but came from before— it was an invention of the political activist website First Draft News, which is partially funded by Google.4

Propagandists were invited into the news-room. We're in the midst of an information war where it's difficult to tell the truth from lies. Journalists are no longer watchdogs. They are taking information from sources with agendas and then trying to convince the public of whatever today's lie is. Censorship and "debunking" are now standard operating procedures.

Efforts are underway to program the public to request that their information be censored and "fact-checked" by agents with an agenda.

When you only hear one side of the story, and you can't access contrary information, it becomes impossible to decipher what is real.

While there used to be a firewall between reporters and the people they reported on, that's long gone. Propagandists are now part of the media.

The COVID false information campaign. In early 2020, as the pandemic first started brewing, it was painfully obvious to investigative journalist Sharyl Attkisson that the public narrative was a pack of lies. Many scientists she spoke to were questioning the advice being given by government scientists. Fauci, director of the National Institute of Allergy and Infectious Diseases and lead spokesperson for the president's COVID response, was questionable early on. She asked the scientists if they would speak out about their concerns, but:

> They said they dared not speak out for fear of being controversialized and for fear of being called coronavirus deniers because that phrase was starting to be used in the media. And secondly, they feared contradicting Fauci, who they said had been canonized in the press.

These scientists' opinions deserved to be heard, but their fears of losing their government funding and their careers silenced them.

Attkisson went on:9 "That started to strike me as, this is a really dangerous environment when esteemed scientists who have valuable information and opinions are afraid to give them, and instead we're hearing a party line that many of them disagree with but won't say so."

She mentioned the controversial U.S. government funding of gain-of-function research in China, and the notion that SARS-CoV-2 could have come from a Chinese laboratory — both were glaring issues that no one would talk about.

"These are the kinds of things early on that were sort of a red flag to me that says somebody's trying to shape the information," she continued. "They're using reporters to do it. Public health figures are involved and that makes me want to know what's really behind it."10

The term 'Conspiracy Theory' was devised by the CIA. It is now used to dismiss narratives that go against the grain. According to Attkisson, it is intentional. These words were originally used by the CIA to debunk theories about the assassination of JFK.

She writes, "Agents (were to) go out and talk to reporters

about these things as conspiracy theories. I'm married to a former law enforcement official who has said to me many times, you know the conspiracy theory phrase as it is used doesn't make sense. Nearly everything is a conspiracy."11

Anything that involves two or more people is technically a conspiracy, but now when people hear the term, they're conditioned to think it's false. Attkisson goes on, "It's designed to pluck this little part of your brain that says, 'well that thing's not true.'" When she hears the term, however, she thinks that information may well be true. "If somebody's trying to debunk it, it usually means a powerful interest is behind it and it makes me want to go search for more information."

The term "conspiracy theory" has lost meaning now because it's used so much. "Debunked", "quackery" and "antivaccine" are all terms that are similarly being used as propaganda tools. Attkisson says, "There's a whole cast of propaganda phrases that I've outlined that are cues. When you hear them, they should make you think, 'I need to find out more about it,'"

Fact checkers try to discredit an accurate BMJ investigation. In another example of the lengths that fact-checkers will go to discredit a story — even if it's true — take an article published in the BMJ, titled, "COVID-19: Researchers blows the whistle on data integrity issues in Pfizer's vaccine trial."12 Written by investigative journalist Paul D. Thacker, it details a series of problems with laboratory management and quality control checks by Pfizer subcontractor Ventavia Research Group, which was testing Pfizer's COVID-19 vaccine.

A regional director formerly employed by Ventavia witnessed falsified data, unblinded patients, inadequately trained vaccinators, and lack of proper follow-up on reported adverse events. After repeatedly notifying Ventavia about her concerns, she made a complaint to the U.S. Food and Drug Administration. She was fired the same day.13

Soon after Thacker's investigative piece was published in BMJ, it was "fact-checked" by a group called Lead Stories, which called her investigation a "hoax alert." Along with "correcting" statements that Thacker did not make, Lead Stories claimed the investigation had "missing context." Investigative reporter Matt Taibbi explained, "'Missing context' has become a term to disparage reporting that is true but inconvenient."

Lead Stories took further issue with the BMJ investigation because it was shared by people such as Dr. Robert Malone and Robert F. Kennedy, who themselves have been targeted by fake fact-checkers. Taibbi added:15

"The real issue with Thacker's piece is that it went viral and was retweeted by the wrong people. As Lead Stories noted with marked disapproval, some of those sharers included the likes of Dr. Robert Malone and Robert F. Kennedy. To Lead Stories, this clearly showed that the article was bad somehow, but the problem was, there was nothing to say the story was untrue."

Thacker also called the "fact check" against his BMJ investigation "insane," telling Taibbi:16 "Here's what they do. They're not fact-checking facts. What they're doing is checking narratives. They can't say that your facts are wrong, so it's like, 'Aha, there's no context.' Or, 'It's misleading.' But that's not a fact check. They just don't like the story."

Reality is being altered in real-time. As it stands, information is being changed in real-time to meet a common agenda. This includes definitions in dictionaries and on official government websites. Examples of definitions that have been changed recently include those for the pandemic, herd immunity, vaccines, and anti-vaxxer. Attkisson goes on:

> Virtually every form of information and sourcing that can be co-opted has been. That even includes the dictionary definitions and many other sources because these are important ways to influence thought. Language is powerful. People don't want to be affiliated with certain names and labels.
>
> It reminds me of '1984,' the George Orwell story about the futuristic society, under which history was being rewritten in real-time to jive with the version that the government or the party wanted it to be. Definitions are now being rewritten and changed in real-time to fit with the establishment's desired vision.

For now, you can still use the Internet Archive, commonly known as Archive.org, as a historical archive. In addition to digitally hosting more than 1.4 million books and other documents, Archive.org acts as a historical vault for the Internet, preserving cached versions of websites that are no longer accessible to the public.18

Archive.org's Wayback machine preserves digital information that has been removed or deleted, whether intentionally or for other reasons, but it, too, might disappear one day. Attkisson says:19

> It's been a fascinating way to prove the effort to change our perception. All we really have now is the electronic record, by and large, and if that can be manipulated, there could be a time when — if they get rid of the

Wayback machine, for example — that we can't ever prove that anything had changed.

Attkisson is maintaining a running list of things the media or public policy got wrong during the pandemic. These can still be verified using the Wayback machine, but they are not acknowledged as having been " corrected" by the press. They include:20

- Claims that the lab theory about the release of coronavirus had been debunked, when it had not been debunked
- Public health officials saying masks don't work, and then saying masks do work
- Fauci testifying to congress that the death rate for coronavirus was 10 times worse than the flu, yet Attkisson found a published article by Fauci where he said the opposite, that "the overall clinical consequences of COVID-19 may ultimately be more akin to those of a severe seasonal influenza"21
- It was wrong to send infected people from hospitals to nursing homes
- It was wrong to isolate at home and close down parks and beaches; early data from New York City showed the vast majority of people hospitalized with coronavirus had been isolated at home, while people outside were not getting sick
- It was wrong to tell people to wash their groceries off to prevent COVID-19

- It was wrong to say COVID-19 shots prevented infection and transmission, and that the shots prevented 100% of hospitalizations and deaths
- It was wrong to not focus more on therapeutics prior to shots and also post-shots

You can be controlled if you live inside the internet "box." Attkisson references a whole generation of people who live inside the box. Those who rely solely on the internet for their information are at serious risk of being controlled. She explains:22

> They didn't know a time when information could be gathered elsewhere by looking around, seeing what you hear, seeing what you saw, talking to people around you, and looking at books and research. And the people that want to control the information understand that if they can just control a few basic sources including Google, Twitter, Facebook, and Wikipedia where they have a lock on the information because we've all been funneled to those few sources. That has been the goal all along.
>
> There's a whole lot of people that get pretty much everything they know through the internet. And the goal of the people trying to make the narrative is to make people live online and to think that's reality." The danger of this is that the internet paints a different picture from reality. You may read something that doesn't sound quite right, or that you don't agree with, but the internet makes you feel like you're in the minority — even if you're are not.

Attkisson goes on:

Understand that you may actually be in the majority, ... but the goal of what they do online is to make you think you're an outlier when you're not, to make you afraid to talk about your viewpoint because they want to control you and make you think you're the one who's crazy You can be made to believe that — if you live in the box. So, I'm constantly telling people to live outside the box. Yes, you can get information there and do what you do online, but trust your common sense and talk to people around you. If you travel, talk to the people in the places you go. You'll get a whole different picture, as I do, of what's happening.

The truth will find a way to be told. While there are powerful forces at play to control information, all is not lost. Attkisson is aware of three entities that are actively working on a solution, which include:

- Investors who want independent news organizations
- Technical people trying to invent platforms that can't be controlled and deplatformed by Big Tech
- Journalists who want to work or contribute to these efforts

The Substack.com newsletters and the video platforms Rumble, Bitchute, and Odysee are getting around Big Tech censorship. But Attkisson believes that censorship will accelerate in the next few years:

The propagandists may have overplayed their hand by being so obvious about the control of information and their censorship. It's no longer deniable. Even people who want their sources curated can't be always happy with the notion that they're not able to get the full story, or that they're only getting one side of something. I think the truth finds a way to be told ... while there are a lot of people who are willing to be fooled, humans seek the truth. Follow your own common sense and reason.

Do your own research, make up your own mind, and trust your intuition. You're going to be right more often than you think. Read a lot, think a lot, and don't buy into the face value of any narrative. View "fact checking, conspiracy theory, and misinformation" as badges of fraud—indicators that you are hearing lies.

Chapter 10
Diversion: TMI About Yoho (con't)

I f you search for my name, you will be treated to salacious accounts of my various lawsuits, medical board "accusations," and other defamations. Judge me by my history:

The following describes my last years in practice (from the preface of *Butchered by "Healthcare"*).

In the summer of 2013, when I was 61, I had two women in their 30s die in my surgical center. I sent them to the emergency room, but nothing worked. It was my place, so I was responsible. It was the worst period of my life. I felt guilty and was sleepless, and my wife thought we would have to give up our practice.

I did not learn why it happened until the autopsy reports came back fully six months later. One woman had an embolus of fat blocking her lungs. This occurs unpredictably, and there is no way to prevent it.

The second had a high local anesthetic blood level. We inject this drug into fat to decrease pain, and after liposuction, we sometimes transplant the fat back into the breasts and buttocks. This may have raised her levels and caused her death, but there was no way to be sure.

I started reading medicine twenty to thirty hours a week to occupy my mind. My original training was as a generalist, but I had studied only cosmetic surgery for decades.

I began with the Prozac-class antidepressants, which I had prescribed since their invention. It stunned me to learn they hardly worked and were often damaging. I read further and found that other psychiatric medications produce irreversible brain and health problems. Doctors have been trained to pass them out like jelly beans.

I learned that many drugs are given for wholly theoretical, even speculative, benefits. Many are damaging. I consulted people for cosmetic surgery who were taking ten (10) of these at once. I began to see how medical corporations had done this to us.

I read about back pain. Most of it goes away on its own, but doctors had been thoughtlessly prescribing opioid painkillers and turning many patients into struggling addicts. Low back surgeries are the most expensive and some of the least effective procedures in all medical care, bar none. No one admits this even to themselves—not the surgeons, the hospital administrators, or the surgical centers' owners. The enormous profits short-circuit everybody's judgment.

I also realized that over the past three decades, younger and younger people had been getting heart disease, obesity, and diabetes. I wondered if healthcare, particularly medication use, might be the cause. I thought about Peter Van Etten's line, "In this insanity of healthcare, the patient always loses." I saw that we were breaking them on a medical torture wheel.

The California Medical Board put me on probation, which required a string of expenses and indignities, and I resolved to quit if I had another patient problem. After this inevitably happened, I resigned my license at the average age when physicians retire, 65. The Board could no longer harass me, and I did not have to worry about the insurance company jacking my rates up. The last lawsuit was finally settled in July 2022, three years after I quit.

Medical boards are supposed to monitor and sometimes cull out bad physicians. During my career, California's Board metastasized up to a budget of about 60 million dollars a year, all harvested from the doctors. They censure fully half of us during our careers. The "Medical Practice Act" that governed physician conduct was a slender booklet when I came to California but the size of a telephone book when I quit.

The Board had become an out-of-control bureaucracy with a captive court system specializing in monkey trials and intimidation. They are now directed to censure those who "spread misinformation." This includes recommending ivermectin for Covid or telling the truth about the vax. But later, as I watched physicians aid and abet the Covid tragedy, I realized that any retribution inflicted on us was too little, too late.

The following is why I decided to write *Butchered by "Healthcare"* (from Chapter 1):

I have affluent peers, and many are not shy about it. A gastroenterologist boasted in the doctors' lunchroom that he puts diamonds on the fingers of his infant daughters.

In 2004, a cardiologist wearing a $3000 suit told me he "could not pay his personal expenses" if he made less than $600,000 a year. Nouveau riche posturing like this is usually accompanied by stories about expensive, supposedly lifesaving treatments. I always vaguely smelled a rat, but I was busy and never gave it much thought.

As I continued to study, I realized that newer science proved many of the therapies these people were selling were worthless. I wondered what profit their fancy cars or high incomes could be for them if they did not put patients first.

After much personal and professional reflection, I decided to write about the whole medical-industrial calamity. I understand I am a whistleblower, what it means, and what I face. In late 2019, I retired and left the melee. I can now say what I need to from outside the tent without conflicts of interest.

It took me three years to do the research and develop the writing skills to tell the story. I worked through one brutal fact after another. Much of it was the agonizing effort of trying to pretend that it was not all true. By the end, I was contemptuous of my peers and of what medicine had become. And I knew that although I had taken care of my family, I had wasted my potential by playing doctor all my life.

Next is Part 3, The Covid and Vax Disasters. If you want to listen to a late 2022 summary video about it, HERE is the link.

Part Three
The COVID and Vax Disasters

Chapter 11
"Hot Lots" Make the Covid Vax Russian Roulette

It was a situation for despair, but there was no alternative but to keep one's nerve.

> — Colonel Heinz-Gunther Guderian, a German Panzer tank commander who was facing the Allied invaders on D-day

I f you play Russian Roulette by spinning a six-shot revolver's cylinder using one bullet, your chance of dying is one in six. If you play Covid vax roulette, your chance of dying or being mortally wounded is about one in 200. The following is how to calculate your odds.

This is derived from Craig Paardekooper's Covid vaccine VAERS database analysis. HERE is the video showing his graphs and explanations.

Robert Yoho, MD (ret)

SUBSTACK LINK

VAERS, the Vaccine Adverse Event Reporting System, is the US government database that records the vaccine adverse events (AEs) reported by doctors and others. It is an incomplete but immense sample that lists the batches or "lots" for each company in the order they appeared. It also shows AEs by lot number and date of occurrence. The data is primarily from the USA.

"Hot lot" is a research phrase that the vax makers wish you would never hear. The original meaning was a defective product, such as baby spinach recalled for salmonella contamination. To understand what is happening with the Covid vaccine, imagine the food companies trying different doses of salmonella to determine how much damage they would cause. Paardekooper's analysis is robust evidence that the Pharma companies used us like lab rates to test their poisons.

He analyzed the Covid jab harms recorded by VAERS and created the charts below, and I copied them from his video. His work is overwhelming evidence that the three manufacturers coordinated dose-response experiments to measure the toxicity and deaths from different batches of their drugs. Vials without the poisons were likely used as controls.

The odds of the results described below happening by chance alone seem nonexistent, but do not take my word for it. Look at the following summary, the references, and the videos.

The entire study is shown in the first slide below. The horizontal axis is time, and the experiment was run over most of 2021. Each blue dot is a manufacturing batch or lot that includes thousands of bottles with the same contents and serial number. The higher on the vertical axis a blue dot appears, the more deaths and other AEs were reported for the lot.

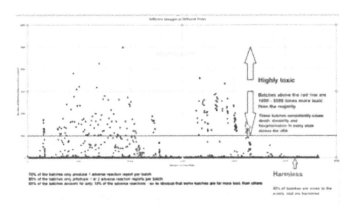

(Degraded quality from video)

Here is what happened

- VAERS recorded 28,330 Covid shot batches or lots.
- About 95 percent of the batches are on the horizontal blue timeline at the bottom. These have few AEs and are relatively harmless. Some are likely saline controls (placebos).

- Although the dots/batches/lots above the blue baseline are all toxic, the "hot lots" above the red line *produce 1000-5000 deaths, disabilities, and other adverse events each and are 3000 to 5000 times riskier than the ones at the baseline.*
- Since the lots above the red line are only .65 percent (.0065) of the total, there is about a 1/200 chance that any given jab contains these very toxic ingredients. After two injections, your chances of getting a bad one doubles. However, your risk of damage or death with subsequent jabs increases much more because the poisons accumulate, which magnifies the risk. In comparison, the risk of dying from most major elective surgeries is 1/1000.
- America was the target of this experiment. The conspirators spread vials from each numbered lot into every state to avoid local disease clusters that might be noticed. When the corporations did not take this precaution, the killer products could sometimes be identified. For example, Wyeth once used a hot lot of DPT vaccines in an area of Tennessee. It killed eight kids and made headlines. After that, the lots were mixed across state lines to make fatality grouping invisible.

Who did it? Pfizer, J & J, or Moderna? Yes.

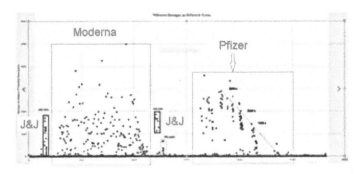

The same graph, annotated.

Johnson and Johnson ran the first tests. Their results are in the small red rectangle on the left. Next, casualties from Moderna are shown in the left-hand square. J and J did a brief second test (the middle red rectangle). Pfizer took over during the second half of the experiment, and their deaths and injuries are shown in the right-hand box.

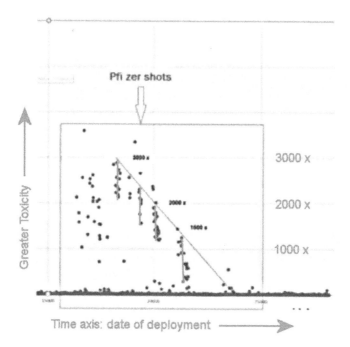

Detail: Pfizer's testing period from the right (later) half of the chart, annotated.

Pfizer's strict quality control is evidence they were running a death study.

- Pfizer seems to have systematically deployed batches of varying toxicity and lethality during the last half of the trial.
- The adverse reactions for each toxic lot, as revealed by the height of the blue dots above the baseline, *are clustered in a limited vertical range and marked in the above graph by the vertical red lines.* These likely reflect individual dosages that were deployed over each limited period.

- These results fit along the slanted plot line above. This is striking evidence that Pfizer started with a higher dose at the start (to the left), then decreased it in five steps over the study period. *It looks exactly like an injury and lethality dose-response study.*
- Between each dose tested, there was a "clear" interval. Here, non-toxic, possibly placebo injections seem to have been used, and the adverse events declined to the baseline blue line. When the injuries and deaths from the lots are plotted, the trends are obvious.

Explaining this data with chance alone is far-fetched. The most likely explanation is it was a study designed to show that higher doses of these poisons injure and kill more people. We were—and are—being slaughtered like guinea pigs, and the perpetrators used the open US VAERS database to monitor their genocide.

Comment

Evidence, settlements, and convictions document big Pharma's long history of mass murder and racketeering. They have their own Wikipedia page of shame about it.

Craig Paardekooper's data suggest that the three companies conspired under joint direction to plan and execute another Holocaust. Some sources estimate that by October 2022, the Covid vax will have killed 20 million people worldwide and injured 2.2 billion others.

How could anyone trust a vaccine of any kind after seeing this, particularly one containing mRNA, such as the new influenza vaccine? How could anyone trust any products made by these companies? Pfizer, Johnson & Johnson, and Moderna.

If this work is accurate, these people are psychopaths. But evil as they are, they are likely only pawns of the global predators directing them.

Craig-Paardekooper's call-out to doctors, nurses, and teachers about the vax:

Please check https://www.howbadismybatch.com/ before allowing your child to receive Covid 19 vaccine.

Doctors and nurses can now check the number of deaths and disabilities reported for any vaccine batch before prescribing it. This way, they can provide better-informed consent before administering from a particular batch.

Every teacher involved in the vaccine deployment should be educating the students about vaccine safety, which means telling the students and parents the reported fatality numbers. Teachers can do this anonymously by texting parents using a different sim. Just send a short message to parents saying, "Vaccine Safety App -"

THIS video describes how to use the website.

Commentary by Dr. Mike Yeadon, former Pfizer executive from THIS source:

If you go from effectively nothing to the worst outcomes ever reported to VAERS, I am prepared to state and to prove that that means it's not the same material in the lots that produce bad side effects.

These drug companies are highly professional outfits. They know how to manufacture reproducibly, and we saw that with the flu vaccines over decades. They know how to do it; they haven't done it...

I'm afraid I've come to the conclusion that they're doing it on purpose, because they're so professional, and after a year they know this data. This data is their window onto the world. They can go into VAERS; they can filter for their own products, and their own lot and batch numbers; and they can see what's happening. They know. So the fact they haven't stopped this tells me that they're at least okay with it—and I fear that this is deliberate...

I've described it to other people by saying, "I'm worried that this is the calibration of a killing weapon." (Yoho's emphasis) [What if, soon,] there are vaccines that would be, say, ten times more lethal than Covid [jabs]—so killing one in a hundred people instead of one in a thousand, roughly: they could just move along and just deploy [bad] batch X or batch Y or batch Z, and that [mass death] is what would happen.

Sources

- Second author credit for this article: my collaborator Sherman.
- To repeat, see https://www.howbadismybatch.com/ for everything about the vax.
- A Midwestern Doctor's Substack HERE describes similar events during the anthrax vaccination campaign.
- James Hill, MD, and Jessica Rose have also posted about this topic.
- If you can tolerate still more evidence, the following video proves that Pfizer's batch codes were numbered sequentially according to their toxicity. Access it HERE.
- A Midwestern Doctor found an analysis from Sweden's data which appears to show Pfizer is also testing hot lots there. This had been censored, so I dug it out of the Wayback Machine.

Chapter 12
SADS, SIDS, and Long-Hauler are Vax Injuries

Covid shots are "medicine" in the same way that thalido-
mide and ice pick lobotomies are "medicine". Approved
as "safe and effective," but a crime against humanity in
actual practice.

— Toby Rogers

Sudden Adult Death Syndrome (SADS), the Covid
long-hauler syndrome, and sudden infant death
syndrome (SIDS) are all caused by vaccinations.
These fake diagnoses were concocted to cover up the countless Covid and childhood vaccine injuries. Chaval, Pierre
Kory, and Mercola explain.

Note: The end of this essay has treatment recommendations.

* * *

SUDDEN ADULT DEATH Syndrome is a fraud

Wikipedia censors negative information about the clot shot, so they do not mention it in their article about SADS:

> Sudden adult death syndrome (SADS), sudden unexplained death syndrome (SUDS), and sudden unexpected nocturnal death syndrome (SUNDS), are sudden, unexpected deaths of adolescents and adults, mainly during sleep... [This] can be caused by medication, myocarditis, cardiac conduction disease, genetic connective tissue disorders, or other causes.

But they kindly show us what your EKG would look like if SADS caused ventricular fibrillation and killed you:

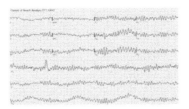

Nice to know, right?
SUBSTACK LINK

* * *

CHAVAL, an anonymous author, explains

Countless adults 40 years and younger are dropping dead, and authorities are calling this Sudden Adult Death Syndrome. This new, supposedly mysterious disease has been recognized by insurance companies, independent media, and some physicians.

Left unsaid, but playing out in the data is that these young people are passing away in the prime of their lives after having been vaccinated with one or more Covid inoculations. There has not been a single case report of an unvaccinated person in this age group suddenly dropping dead without another cause.

Over the past two years, doctors, immunologists, and virologists around the globe have been warning about the Covid vaccine. They predicted myocarditis and a host of other diseases. They also foretold "antibody deficiency enhancement," which is a decline in immunity to Covid infection after the "vaccination."

These mRNA injections have been proven to stimulate prolonged manufacture of spike protein in the host's body. This produces many ill effects, including clots in the blood, heart, brain, and other organs. How long this continues is unknown, but what is clear is that if a patient is "boosted" more than once, the risk multiplies.

SADS resembles SIDS (Sudden Infant Death Syndrome). The SIDS name was coined decades ago to label the epidemic of infants dying suddenly without a recognized cause.

With this background, the old mystery of what causes SIDS has become apparent. It was a hoax created to explain away injuries caused by childhood vaccines. A new study of SIDS data since the 1990s based on the Vaccine Adverse Response System (VAERS) found that nearly every baby dying from SIDS received a childhood vaccination within 1-7 days before passing away. (78.3 % occurred within 7 days post-vaccination) The SIDS label had fooled us so thoroughly and for so long that someone hatched the SADS swindle to dupe us again. And, just like they did for SIDS, the legacy media and medical journals are trying to normalize SADS.

As of this writing, there have been 28,532 post-vaccination deaths reported in VAERS and over 1.287 million adverse reactions. A Harvard study of VAERS showed that the actual figures could be as high as 10 to 40 times that. Many nurses are saying that they were ordered not to report these events. And according to CDC whistleblowers, the agency has removed as many as 12,500 records of the most serious cases from the database. Finally, the media fails to report that the vaccine injury compensation programs are overwhelmed.

Most of us know a healthy person who died suddenly without warning. We have also heard about celebrities and professional athletes dropping dead. Single-car "vaccidents" have been rising, and previously healthy pilots have mysteriously suffered career-ending ailments. Several have died hush-hush in midflight.

A Pharma executive, Jose Maria Fernandez Sousa-Faro, recently paid for a vaccine passport and was injected with saline. Industry insiders say that many athletes and celebrities have done this as well. The elitists' hypocrisy is plain to see and tells you all you need to know about vaccine safety.

Unless you have intentionally chosen to ignore the obvious evidence for two years, you understand that the clot shots do not prevent the spread of Covid, do not prevent infection, and are not vaccines in the traditional sense;

rather, they permanently alter genes. The jab has profound risks and no net benefit.

What we see now has been described as Stockholm Syndrome, mass formation psychosis, or cognitive dissonance. Some people are willfully ignorant, but the legacy media and the medical community are powerful propaganda machines that have hypnotized a full third of us. Other people are falling into line to avoid being socially chastised. They would prefer to take a jab that might maim or kill them than to buck the systems or personal relationships.

* * *

THE COVID LONG-HAULER SYNDROME is another coverup invented to conceal Covid vax injury, by Pierre Kory

From Pierre Kory's Reports. He is a major contributor who has invented and educated others about treatments for intensive care patients.

It took me a while to figure out why no patient in my hospital's intensive care unit (ICU) ever had their vaccination status on the front screen of their record. It was instead stuck in the nursing notes where no one would look for it. I also learned that patients who had "unknown vax status" were being designated "unvaccinated." Patients dying of Covid within two weeks of getting the shot were also called unvaccinated.

These methods persuaded doctors and nurses that everyone in the hospital was unvaccinated. It also allowed our federal health agencies to create and disseminate charts showing that hospitals were filled with the unvaccinated. They further manipulated even this false data.

These widespread frauds encouraged doctors to hector anyone and everything to get injected.

An ICU nurse sent me the following:

> My friends on the night shift had stories to share about patients. All of them confirmed what we've seen—none of it makes sense unless you go to the 800 pound elephant in the room, the vaccine. We have not heard a peep from the vax cheerleaders on staff recently. I know some have buyer's remorse for pushing their family to get vaxxed, but there's no need to dig into that wound now. Long Covid is the only term allowed, never vax injury.

Her last line really got to me. The standard practice is to blame all the strange illnesses on "Long hauler Covid" rather than "vaccination injury syndrome." She continues:

> Many employees, as well as patients, are participating in a Long Covid study - I know two employees in it. Don't know that it is providing them with any answers to their disabling issues, especially at their young age, but they're hopeful. They are true believers - they got fully vaxxed and boosted and will continue to do so. And they continue to contract Covid variants and pass them along to the rest of the same vaxxed-up cohort. Rinse and repeat. To bring up data that points to the exponential and cumulative harm is just pointless. They want to die on the hill of believing they did the right thing, no matter what their bodies are telling them, until they can no longer do so.

I pulled aside an ED doc, but we had to go outside to

talk. And yes, our phones were off. In ED, patient issues are discussed in a kind of code if it concerns vax injury as the probable cause. Administrators wander through at all hours, so open discussions are not happening.

Residents are getting frustrated - I heard it's coming out in staff meetings because they are seeing data, and patients are bringing in data. Shift hand-off reports can get tense, I was told. Many are suffering from cognitive dissonance, "I have hundreds of thousands in med-school loans. I cannot deviate, or I lose everything and still have to pay back all that money. Must stick to what I am told." They become check-box doctors. You either sell your soul or seek your own data and then join the "French Medical Resistance." This is not an easy call for a 20-something to make.

Not every patient is willing to walk in the dark about the severe issues they are having and believe the primary care physicians telling them there is nothing to worry about. The pushback from patients who decide to be informed is real, and the emergency docs have to find a way to address it before they admit or discharge a patient with some vague diagnosis. I see future liability expanding as the data keeps coming out. More patients are asking for their FULL medical records. They know. They know.

All the other stuff is still happening. We still have no space in the cancer hospital side for the explosion of pts needing treatment for their vax injuries - and it is NOT because they delayed cancer therapy due to the pandemic. It is NOT from delayed screening or treatment initiation. It's because they just received a new diagnosis that requires immediate intervention.

According to the same case manager I spoke with

weeks ago who is carrying a patient load of almost 1000 now, she is trying to get creative and find space at outpatient facilities closed on weekends and schedule her teams and patients to go there. Those sites have full equipment, so they can give infusions at least. This is crazy. She called asking if we could open up space in another area - and yes, we are doing it.

Unsurprisingly, the diseases caused by the vax are still an unsolved mystery at Wikipedia: "While studies into various aspects of long Covid are underway, as of November 2021, the definition of the illness is still unclear, as is its mechanism."

Yoho note: HERE is another reference. Covid long hauler syndrome can happen without the vax, but most cases are closely related.

* * *

MERCOLA: VACCINATION INJURIES AND THE FLCCC TREATMENT PROTOCOL

By Joseph Mercola, published June 18, 2022, on the Mercola blog. Here is the original PDF.

"My heart is so broken, I cannot keep quiet anymore," Marik said, choking back tears during a Children's Health Defense hearing in Ohio where several vaccine-injured patients also shared their tragic journeys. "This is a humanitarian crisis! These people are suffering. This is real disease."

Patients injured by the Covid jab say they receive little help when they go to the hospital. There are no specialized vaccine injury clinics. They have trouble getting care anywhere.

In the meantime, Pierre Kory's Front Line Covid Critical Care Alliance (FLCCC) is sharing their I-RECOVER protocol in the hope that doctors will begin to treat Covid jab injuries appropriately.

Dr. Kory states that Covid-19 is no longer an emergency. The true emergency is the continued use of the Covid vaccines, which are causing injuries on an alarming, unprecedented level.

He cites life insurance data showing historic rises in excess deaths for young people. The vaccine injuries reported to the U.S. Vaccine Adverse Event Reporting System (VAERS) are further support. Kory says that according to some estimates, 500,000 Americans have lost their lives because of these shots. And the most highly vaccinated and boosted nations are experiencing record case and death rates from Covid compared to countries with lower injection rates.

Treatment of vaccine injuries

Regardless of where the spike protein comes from — the shot, the virus, or close contact shedding — it produces many ill effects. The jab is the worst because it stimulates the body to make still more toxic protein. Whether this ever stops is unknown, but early, aggressive, and appropriate treatment can help. This lowers the spike protein in the blood and reduces the risk of prolonged post-vax symptoms that the mainstream calls long-haul Covid.

The jabs damage immune function, which is the first line of defense against all diseases. Appendicitis and pediatric hepatitis have recently increased. Several rare forms of cancer have also become more common; some are aggressive and fast-moving. In late 2021, pathologist Dr. Ryan Cole reported a 20-fold increase in endometrial cancer as well as a "massive uptick" in autoimmune diseases.

Ivermectin works well for the majority, while others benefit little. This drug has been used safely for over 50 years. A large-scale Brazilian trial studied people who received ivermectin for four days every month for six months. Not only were the chances of contracting Covid reduced dramatically, but kidney and liver function improved.

Dr. Kory says that both published studies and experience with patients prove that ivermectin is exceptionally safe. Marik adds, "It's one of the safest medications ... even when taken in high doses appropriately."

FLCCC vaccine injury protocol: first line

The information below is a summary. Refer to this PDF link for the complete document.

Ivermectin — 0.2 to 0.3 mg/kg, daily for up to 4 to 6 weeks. For best absorption, this is taken with or just following a meal. Some people respond to it, and others do not. Ivermectin has potent anti-inflammatory properties and binds to the spike protein, which improves its elimination.

Vitamin C — 1000 mg orally three to four times a day. Note: these high doses are not recommended for indefinite daily use. C helps promote the growth of protective gut bacteria. Avoid high dose C in patients with a history of kidney stones.

Vitamin D — reasonable starting doses are 4,000 to 5,000 IU (international units) per day. This should be adjusted by measuring blood levels. (Yoho note: Vitamin D levels for Florida lifeguards can be 120 ng/ml. Getting your levels over 60 ng/ml—or better, near 100 ng/ml—is thought by many authorities to be advantageous. You may need more D than Dr. Mercola advises to accomplish this. Doses are individual.)

Vitamin K — 100 mcg/day.

Quercetin — 250 to 500 mg/day (Mixed flavonoids are an alternative). These are anti-inflammatory. Due to a possible drug interaction between quercetin and ivermectin, these drugs should not be taken at the same meal. In rare cases, quercetin has been associated with hypothyroidism, so it should be used with caution in patients with this problem. Physicians should consider checking thyroid hormone blood levels.

Magnesium — 500 mg/day.

FLCCC vaccine injury protocol: second line.

Hydroxychloroquine (HCQ) 200 mg twice daily for 1–2 weeks, then reduced to 200 mg/day. This is safe during pregnancy. For long-term use and for patients weighing less than 135 pounds, the dose should be reduced to possibly 100 to 150 mg/day.

Intravenous vitamin C — 25 grams once a week. The first weekly IV dose should be lower, 7.5–15 grams. Vitamin C is given slowly IV over 2–4 hours, together with the oral form, 1000 mg 2–3 times per day. Since vitamin C can cause kidney stones, the length of therapy must be limited.

N-acetyl cysteine (NAC) — 600–1500 mg/day.

Low-dose corticosteroid — 10–15 mg/day of prednisone or the equivalent for three weeks. Taper to 10 mg/day and then 5 mg/day as it is discontinued.

For the complete list, see the I-RECOVER Post-Vaccine Treatment Protocol, which is available on Covid19criticalcare.com.

Yoho note: This protocol is predictable and safe, but some of the recommendations from the full list are speculative. You need supervision by a physician. Pierre Kory works full time treating these patients, and he does virtual consultations. Contact him at: Drpierrekory.com. There are also reports of long hauler's syndrome caused by blood transfusions into people who have never had the Covid vaccine. A reader had this happen to her.

* * *

HOW TO ORDER ivermectin and other drugs abroad

First, read what *Butchered by "Healthcare"* says about mail-ordering drugs:

> Since patented medications are more dependable than generics, look for them overseas. Most manufacturers sell their patented drugs in other countries at a fraction of the US price, often using another brand name. You can purchase them by mail-order from foreign pharmacies' websites. Some are over-the-counter there, making this easy.
>
> Some drugs are 50 to even 98 percent less costly than in the US. For example, in late 2017, the brand name Viagra was $65 here for a single 100 mg tablet and $30 for the authorized generic. By early 2020, Good-Rx.com, which compares US-based pharmacies, was offering this generic for around $12. Check for updates on their website. But various Indian websites sell the same medication for $1. I have a close friend who tried the Indian version, and he said it was a little weak but worked fine.
>
> The drug industry calls this reimportation, and they aggressively oppose it, supposedly to protect quality. Several state governments have championed their citizens' rights to order abroad, however. There were congressional fights in the early 2000s to make this

lawful nationwide, but our bought-and-paid-for legislature continues to block it. The compromise seems to be
to leave it illegal but not prosecute anyone.

Since the FDA does not reach out of the US, there
are more quality issues abroad. A maker might fake a
brand name. A generic might have no active ingredients
or even contain contaminants. But by 2014, wholesalers
were importing 80 percent of the drugs and ingredients
used here, anyway. European pharmacies get most of
their drugs from other countries as well.

PharmacyChecker.com can tell you if the medications ordered overseas are likely OK. The best policy is
always caveat emptor. Learn as much as you can before
you buy, and observe the effects of anything you take. Be
just as careful at Walgreens as when buying interna-
tionally.

The following is a pharmacy in India that sells many
drugs, including ivermectin. I have heard good things about
them, but there are never guarantees about the legality of
ordering medicines overseas or about their quality.
Sunrise Enterprise
export@sunriseindia.org
A-206, 2nd Floor, Sumel Business Park-6
Dudheshwar Road
Opposite Hanumanpura BRTS, Shaibaug
Ahmedabad, State-Gujarat (India)
Whatsapp - +919099096658

Chapter 13
What Insider Nurses Are Saying About the Covid Vaccination Crisis

In a time of universal deceit, telling the truth is a revolutionary act.

— Often attributed to George Orwell

By movement hero Pierre Kory, MD, MPA.
The massive propaganda campaign that led doctors to disassociate from recognizing widespread vaccine injuries is weakening. A stark reality is finally creeping in.

SUBSTACK LINK

A text to Dr. Kory from a nurse on May 12, 2022:

I have had 20 yrs + experience—ICU - cardiac, neuro ICU/ neurosurgical ICU mostly, and ED at Level 1. I was vax injured from 2 Pfizer doses mandated by my major University hospital system. Clotting issues, open bleeding, spontaneous with no ability to stop, weeping down arms and legs. Severe leg clot post-surgery in March.

Had to get D-Dimer ordered by force at the little ED I was in and use my own portable doppler I brought in from work b/c they had no Ultrasound techs or equipment access - TPA (clot buster med) finally. Cervical lymph nodes enlarged since vax especially, for over 1.5 yrs. Cannot biopsy at least one as it sits on my Left carotid, now wrapped around it,

Got Covid originally while working ED in March 2020. "N antibody" is still high as of Nov 2021. Hit neuro, never respiratory. Had the same issues with H1N1 vaccine, which was also mandated, and then I got Guillain Barre Syndrome and neurological weakness - out of work five months. Will not get any boosters or vaccines this year, but have no exemption as all docs took to the "deer in headlight" look and said nothing. I will lose my career this winter if I refuse. Functional med/family practitioner - she has a long wait list, and I have no idea how she sits with this data on vaccine injured.

My VAERS report - it was deleted. The pharmacist never entered as required, so I did. It has vanished. My batch numbers - are significant for bad neurologic responses, and clotting.

Cassandra's Memo

I lost my Hematologist-Oncologist doctor to a vaccine injury - he is out and never to practice again - in his early 40s. He was a "true believer" and in denial until it was he who was the injured patient. Our cancer hospital - I know most of the case managers and many doctors since they were residents. They now have case-loads in the 1000s rather than 250-400 over any given quarter. Not enough beds or infusion space for cancer patients as outpatients. Radiation treatment backlog. All at a huge cancer hospital monstrosity itself. All kinds - brain, lymph, stomach, pancreas, blood, AND EYE CANCERS - orbital, especially in younger people recently vaxxed.

Microvascular ischemia on the rise in vaxxed younger people. Strokes way up in no-risk, no co-morbidities, young to younger-ish. Ask me anything. I'll give you an inside scoop from the floors and suites. This has to stop. They need to admit the fraud and crime and STOP. The liability must be lifted, and mandates ended. They KNOW NOW, and many KNEW THEN. Don't know if you'll even read this, but I follow all of you on substack and Twitter - those not banned yet! - and read ALL the data. I've been a lab rat myself from an issue from a car accident yrs back - I know the process. So much fraud. Keep going. Never give up. Never, never, never give up. Thank you for all you do, hope that you inspire and the confirmation of that little voice in me that said there was NO way back. Everything was off. I did not have an option or data then. I have data now, and it will keep coming. The option is NO...

Lost four practitioners to serious side effects of "strongly encouraged" boosters. 2 hospitalized, one in MICU. The irony is that most staff are completely lost

....All in their early 30s to mid-40s. All had Covid previous, N antibodies fully measurable. One female, and one male, both inpatient. Female still nursing newborn...

It's the inside folks who talk to each other, and you have to speak another language depending on who's listening. That has been a skill set unto itself. It's texting, the phone calls from area to area with back stories on patient issues. I was getting texts from my old stat team covering the cardiac catheterization lab - the clots. The clots stunned everyone... it continues. My cardiac units - where I spent the bulk of my nursing years - lung and heart transplant included - have so many anomalies presented with patients that never existed before. Rewriting the script for each new problem never encountered. The constant codes (cardiac arrests). Can't keep up.

Lost quite a few coworkers to either VAX injury itself - took them out of the workforce, OR they resigned/accepted firing or retired once mandates were settled. It's the phone calls I have with my cohorts in the other areas of the system. The real story is in those conversations. The doctors are now admitting to injury is growing, but they can't tell their patients why they are no longer practicing. Losing specialists is a big problem not easily solved.

The signaling coming from management MD/PhD administrators has not been towards what winter will bring but is focused on congratulating everyone on clinical excellence during the last 2 yrs. I think there is great trepidation in their approach because they see the data, and they know the inside info on injury, disability/death of faculty and staff not from Covid itself, but the forced vax. We lost only a few to original Covid, with underlying co-morbidities that made outcomes a given in many cases...

It makes me just stop and by the end of the week, take into account cases of, say, ocular orbital cancer in 20-somethings. Have had 6 in the last two weeks with no Family History or other indicators. Out of the blue, some with brain mets now. All vaxxed unwillingly; all had Covid and recovered fine prior to employer-forced vax. The employers, the areas the patients reside in....nothing in common other than the previous. The actuaries are correct. Excess mortality, let alone whatever-life-left disability. Stunning numbers.

Linda is a fellow spirit, highly experienced in ICU and emergency medicine, and she told me even more disturbing developments, like the fact that on some night shifts, nurse teams are seeing more cardiac arrests in a single shift than ever before and in unprecedented younger age patients. On some shifts, they have had so many that the "crash carts" are rolled straight from one arrest to another because the pharmacy, especially on night shifts, is not able to re-stock fast enough. This situation happened maybe once in my whole career when two arrests happened on the same floor or unit within a short time.

She also told me that night nurse are more openly discussing the vaccine as the cause of what they are seeing (much more than during day shifts, apparently). However, they do this mainly by text and use "code." Their code word for a vaccination injury or cause is "that issue," i.e., in reference to a 22-year-old who suddenly arrested on the hospital ward, "he is having that issue." Note these are nurses.. not the docs.. but some of the docs are talking to her, like the one above who performed six enucleations (eyeball removals) already this year in young people (very rare to have to do this, especially in this age group). She also told me about how her interventional cardiologist nurse friends related that some patients are coming in with massive heart attacks, and during the angiogram, the interventional cardiologists are seeing such extensive thrombi filling the entire artery (as documented by some embalmers), that they say "I can't stent or remove this, this guy needs surgery, like now."

BMGF/WHO/NIH et al. had clearly identified "vaccine hesitancy" as the main enemy in the battle plans they drew up and distributed after their viral pandemic simulation exercises over the past decade (see the RFK, JR., EXPOSES FAUCI, GATES, AND AIDS chapter). In this prominent medical journal publication addressing viral pandemics, they state, "The World Health Organization has listed vaccine hesitancy among the greatest threats to global health, calling for research to identify the factors associated with this phenomenon." Vaccine hesitancy is why the HHS gave $1 Billion to U.S media to support a relentlessly positive public relations campaign supporting the uptake of vaccines.

Falsification of vaccine status

During all of 2021, I had only taken care of one ICU patient who was officially documented in their medical record as "fully vaccinated." This was impossible. I knew this was false based on data from countries that more transparently reported vaccination status and hospital outcomes. In multiple reports starting in February 2021, the majority of hospitalizations and deaths (even when adjusted to rates per 100,000) had long been the vaccinated.

One of the more ridiculous attempts to cover this fraud up in the U.S was a media narrative launched in June/July of 2021 that was created from statements by Fauci and

Wollensky. They said that 99% of patients dying in the hospital were unvaccinated. They included in their numerator all the deaths that occurred prior to the start of the vaccination campaign. Yup, if you died in 2020, you were reported as dying in an unvaccinated status.

Here is how I think they falsely suppressed the real rate of vaccinated patients entering U.S. hospitals and dying. In the most popular electronic medical record system in the U.S. (EPIC), on the sidebar of every page in the chart are the name, demographics, room number, provider team, and Covid vaccination status of the patient. What I found weird from the outset was that, in EPIC, there were only two categories under the Covid-19 vaccine status section, "Vaccinated" or "Unknown." There was no "Unvaccinated" status. Unknown was interpreted by all providers and official data as Unvaccinated.

I suspected that during the hospital admission process, there must have been some sort of barrier to deeming someone "vaccinated." I thought that to be documented as vaccinated on admission, you had to have received the vaccine from a primary care physician's clinic who worked for that same hospital system in a system office and that they had this already documented in the electronic medical record. If you got a vaccine from anywhere else outside that hospital system's clinic, you were assigned an unknown, which was interpreted as unvaccinated.

Linda confirmed this was the case where she worked in a major health system. In a smaller one where she also worked, it was easy to document a patient as vaccinated. The admitting nurse could accept a Walgreens card or even a verbal report from the patient or family. The patient would show up as vaccinated on the main screen.

In the major health system, if the patient received the

vaccine from anywhere but an employed provider's clinic within the health system—even if the patient had a vaccine card on them—she was forced to put it in an "open field" buried on page 2 of the initial nursing assessment. This was invisible to the doctors, and the main screen showed up as unknown, which was interpreted as unvaccinated.

This led most U.S doctors to conclude that the only people dying in hospitals were the unvaccinated. This way, all healthcare workers would get vaccinated out of fear of dying and would also aggressively insist that all their patients and family members be vaccinated. This explains why a large percentage of the population—at least the ones I meet at lectures, conferences, and symposia—no longer trust a "system doctor" or "system hospital," no matter how grand their brand/reputation once was.

The system docs believed what they saw on the electronic record. This, combined with the medical journal propaganda, fooled nearly all the nation's doctors. Their fervor to vaccinate everyone and everything, even patients just recovering from Covid, was something to behold. I saw overt hectoring, harassment, and even rage. Twitter doctors arrogantly propagated the need for vaccination, even for folks who had natural immunity. They were screamed on social media, media, and in journal editorials that you would be OK if you just got vaccinated.

The high-profile docs were the worst. I have little sympathy for them, as many must have been complicit rather than fooled like the rest. These include Eric Topol, Peter Hotez, Alastair McAlpine, Tom Friedan (who I used to deeply admire as NYC Health Department Commissioner), Eric Feigl-Ding-(bat), Jeremy Faust (probably the biggest ignoramus on Twitter, having taken an early lead in that competition when the pandemic broke in 2020), and

Monica Gandhi. Leana Wen was the most active prostitute for the Pharma-captured federal health agencies on mass media.

Then you started to see doctor walk-outs protesting the unvaccinated and increasing numbers of doctors publicly stating they would start refusing to see unvaccinated patients. The Pharma-controlled outlet called Medscape even got an ethicist to argue that it was OK to refuse to treat the unvaccinated.

One of my patients, who is a hospital pharmacist, even told me that at her hospital, the hospitalists were vaccinating patients admitted for Covid as they were being discharged from the hospital. I even heard of a team of clinicians deciding to vaccinate a severely ill Covid patient in the ICU.

I also witnessed aggressive attacks on one of the nation's largest medical-centers staff physician email forums. Doctors "screaming" that everything would be fine if everyone just got the damn vaccine. Deriding anyone bringing forth arguments about untested safety, suspicious efficacy data, and concerns about mandates violating patient autonomy and medical ethics. Anyone who brought forth "adverse data" towards the vaccines was treated with dismissal and a retaliatory posting of selectively favorable data with the imprimatur of the Pharma-captured agencies and Pharma-captured journals. I will never forget this time in the history of medicine.

Last one, a text from a colleague:

Just had dinner with my friend, a colleague friend of his here, Dr XXX renowned YY Physician. PRO Vaccine. He was adamant all physicians should get the vaccine and should not be able to practice without it. Was a trailblazer for the vaccine here. He got boosted around Christmas time, had

Robert Yoho, MD (ret)

a stroke less than a week later, lost his eyesight in one eye, lost his practice, cannot be a doctor any longer, and said undoubtedly it was from the Pfizer vaccine and encouraged all of his doctor friends to max out their disability insurance to protect themselves. I know--not surprising to you, but this guy was so pro-vaccine and clearly admitted his stroke and his loss of eyesight from the vaccine!!

Chapter 14

[I Am] Father to a Murdered Son, Husband to a Murdered Wife

And I will have my vengeance in this life or the next.

— Maximus from *Gladiator*

I am friends with vax-murdered men, and Scott Schara is the father of a daughter murdered in a hospital by physicians cooperating with the national Covid treatment policies. Rob Garmong's wife was slaughtered in much the same way (see Part 4 for their stories.) The Children's Health Defense website describes too many other vax killings to count.

How could anyone have missed the memo about the clot shot's lethal effects? We have VAERS data, country comparisons, and insurance companies' reports. Deaths have increased massively in the entire population, and Senator Ron Johnson reported the military deaths, disabilities, and ongoing coverup. Steve Kirsch has more in this POST. The latest news is the genocide of our unborn grandchildren.

We had suspicions about infertility when we learned

that the spike protein collected in the ovaries and testicles. And we knew that the shots made women's menstrual periods irregular. And that women vaxed during their pregnancies had 7 to 8 times the usual miscarriage rate. But we now know that fewer children are being born since the clot shots were rolled out.

SUBSTACK LINK

In Taiwan, for example, live births have dropped 23 percent (29 percent in another report a few days later). This is a monstrous effect, and the odds against it happening by chance alone are one in trillions (with a T). Not only does the time course of the "vaccine" match, but Taiwan is one of the most heavily jabbed places in the world.

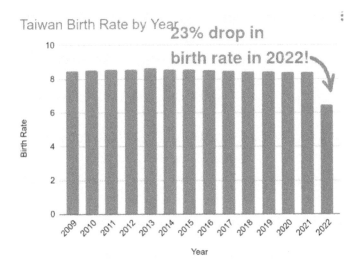

Similar data is coming in from Germany, North Dakota, and Switzerland. European sources in late 2022 show an average drop of over ten percent. Data from the US is scarce.

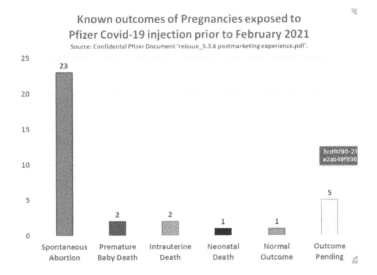

The graph above is from THIS essay.

In Hungary, the most vaccinated counties had the largest drops in birth rates—22 percent since the rollout.

* * *

THE VACCINES DAMAGE FERTILITY. Is this part of a depopulation agenda or 'just' a terrible mistake? From Tess Lawrie's Substack post of June 28, 2022. She is a highly published international health consultant.

Given everything we know about the pandemic—that Covid is eminently treatable, that the vaccines are neither safe nor effective, and that millions have been injured as a direct result—why were the vaccines rolled out and now being allowed to continue?

There are many theories, ranging from the sinister to the plain venal. One of these is that a global elite believes that the planet is overcrowded and has implemented the pandemic and associated vaccine rollout as part of a depopulation agenda.

[Yoho note: read *The Real Anthony Fauci* chapter 12, Germ Games, for how it was all planned. This is reproduced here in the RFK, Jr., chapter in Part 14. The movie is HERE.]

It sounds like the stuff of movies, yet there is a precedent. As Dr. Andrew Wakefield's poignant new documentary, Infertility: A Diabolical Agenda, explains, the World Health Organization spent many years researching and developing vaccines that would render recipients infertile. This line of research came from concern that populations were increasing at an unsustainable rate—and as the documentary reveals, the WHO apparently saw fit to implement its infertility vaccines without the informed consent of the women and girls who received them.

Many concerns have been raised over the impact of Covid-19 vaccines on fertility. The original Pfizer biodistribution studies reveal that the lipid nanoparticle (LNP) used to encapsulate the mRNA does not remain at the injection site as stated but travels to major organs, including the spleen, liver, adrenal glands, and ovaries.

Now, a new peer-reviewed study, accepted for publication in the journal *Andrology*, reveals that Covid-19 vaccines are harming male fertility.

In this study, researchers analyzed samples from three sperm banks in Israel: they evaluated samples before vaccination which served as the baseline control, followed by samples taken periodically for about five months after donors received their second dose of the Pfizer vaccine.

About three months after the second Pfizer dose, sperm concentration was reduced by 15.4%. There was also a percentage change reduction of 22.1% in sperm motility. This is significant: both of these indicators would reduce the chance of sperm fertilizing an egg. (Yoho note: There is more about this HERE.)

The WHO's VigiAccess database holds a growing list of adverse events about reproductive health and fertility, including 5,726 spontaneous abortions, 501 fetal deaths, 208 stillbirths, plus reports of testicular swelling, sexual dysfunction, and many other conditions.

Rather than passive consumers, we are active participants in the glorious web of life, and human fertility is to be treasured as the miracle that it is. If there is even a hint of the vaccines damaging fertility, they must be halted.

* * *

TOBY ROGERS sat through the FDA hearings as they approved the clot shot for babies.

His essay is subtitled, The Government is Coming for Your Kids:

The meetings were surreal as so-called "experts" displayed no critical thinking skills and instead wallowed in clichés supplied to them by the pharmaceutical industry.

When the meetings adjourned for the day, I wandered about the house, trying to make sense of what I had just witnessed, and checked in with friends who were also watching the horror unfold... Then it would be night again, and the cycle would repeat.

Over the course of five meetings in five days, I witnessed crimes against humanity, the end of the bourgeoisie, and the likely end of America...

Those poor [vaccinated] kids will develop a wide range of adverse events — myocarditis, heart attacks, strokes, autoimmune disorders, cancer, endocrine disorders, infertility, and sudden "unexplained" death, to name a few. The over-boosted adults will suffer a similar fate. The bourgeoisie will lose their health, their dignity, and then all of their wealth to the Pharma cartel.

* * *

Yoho notes:

Myocarditis is like a horrible heart attack that may continue for months to years—if you survive. On October 15, 2022, Peter McCullough said that the myocarditis rate has been 25,000 in a million since the vax was deployed. It was four in a million before.

Another reference about deaths is, "UK Government Publishes Horrific Figures on COVID Vaccine Deaths: 1 in Every 310 People Died Within 1.5 Months of Receiving the COVID Vaccine Booster." This is from November 10, 2022, published by 2nd Smartest Guy in the World. Read the original essay at THE EXPOSE and listen to the audio from an earlier article by the same source HERE. This might be a special case or statistical aberration, but the numbers would still be stunning if they were a fraction of what was reported.

For comparison, here are the approximate fatality risks of these surgeries: 1/500 for general surgeries. Gastroplasty has a fatality rate of 1/200. Liposuction is fatal in 1/5,224 to 1/15,3369 procedures, depending on the study. Tummy tucks: 1/600; facelifts: 1/1,000.

Chapter 15
Steve Kirsch is Willing to Have Dinner With Idiots to Save Us

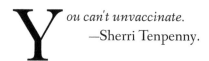Y ou can't unvaccinate.
              —Sherri Tenpenny.

The following is a repost from Steve Kirsch's blog
HERE. *Thank you for your service, Steve.*

Executive summary

People tell me I'm crazy all the time for believing that
the COVID vaccines are unsafe.

But all I am doing is making the obvious conclusions
from all the data in plain sight, including people's reactions
when challenged.

For example, at dinner last night, I revealed that my
occupation was a "myth buster," and then people asked,
"what myth?" and I said that the vaccines were unsafe.
Later, one of the attendees told me I should be ashamed of
myself for spreading misinformation. I asked, "Do you have
any data to back that up?" She said, "I don't want to talk to
you."

Does that sound familiar?

Here's a short checklist of observations that would be very hard to explain if the vaccines are safe and effective.

The sanity checks

The overall sanity check is that all the data (including observing peoples' behavior when challenged) I've seen is consistent with the unsafe hypothesis and not consistent with a very safe vaccine with mild, short-lasting side effects.

Here's a list of data points that suggest that I'm sane in no particular order:

1. **Hundreds of VAERS safety signals are being deliberately ignored by the CDC, including the all-important death safety signal**. This was triggered using the CDC's own methodology, and nobody in the world will acknowledge it. This tells you there is a cover-up.

2. **VAERS is 5.4X underreported for the COVID vaccines compared to earlier vaccines.** When you actually collect the data, you find that VAERS appears to be around 5.4X underreported compared to earlier vaccines. This means that when we find that "acute cardiac failure" is elevated by 475X in VAERS, the actual increase is 2,565X higher than earlier vaccines. So we are probably looking at around 2,500 deaths per million doses of the vaccine. Even if this estimate is off by 100X, this is way past the stopping condition for a safe vaccine.

3. **Healthcare workers observe too many vaccine-related deaths** for this to be a safe vaccine. Just in the first 281 healthcare workers to respond to a survey, they observed over 1,128 vaccine-related deaths. That is not normal. It should be a stopping condition in any normal society. There are over 22 million healthcare workers in America, which is 100,000 times larger than my sample size..

4. **CDC hides from the facts**. The CDC refuses to comment on anything I've written despite the fact that they are focused on reducing the amount of misinformation in order to reduce vaccine hesitancy. They won't even return my calls offering to discuss our disagreements. This makes no sense since in a Google search for "misinformation superspreaders," I'm usually the top result. How do they expect to resolve the open issues by not communicating? They haven't answered that (and the mainstream media won't ask them this obvious question either).

5. **The top US safety officials duck and run for cover when you try to show them adverse safety data.** Scientists are supposed to seek the truth, not duck and run for cover when asked if they want to see safety data. Read this article about ACIP chair Grace Lee. Rather than answer a simple question about whether she wanted to see the confidential Israeli safety data (that the Israeli

government is hiding from the public), she chose to call the police. It's caught on video.

6. **The FDA's Dr. Peter Marks publicly said he'd do anything to reduce vaccine hesitancy.** I said the simplest way is to debate us and show the world how we got it wrong. He declined to do that. I still don't know why. Do you?

7. **There are no debates**. No public health authority or any of the experts relied on by the mainstream media will engage in a debate. We are willing to pay them to attend, but nobody wants to, not for any amount of money.

8. **Even David Gorski, the doctor who prides himself on discrediting misinformation spreaders, won't touch** the VAERS analysis showing that the results cannot be explained by "overreporting." Nor will he verify the fact that VAERS has generated safety signals that nobody noticed, even when I offered him up to $1M to compensate him for his time.

9. **The large number of "black swan events"** in plain sight is simply too high to be consistent with the "safe and effective" claim. These events are typically sudden unexpected deaths or injuries in people.

10. **The messages from the grave** from high profile people. For example, the inventor of the v-safe program Joel Kallman died under very mysterious circumstances after getting his

second dose of the vaccine. He supposedly died from COVID, but he never got COVID. Nobody's talking. See Oracle VP Joel Kallman Dies of "Covid" After Receiving Second Vaccine Injection. This article points out that there was no news that a prominent vaccinated person got COVID.

11. It would be interesting to see Joel Kallman's v-safe record. Why don't they release it?

12. **The Doug Brignole test.** Brignole challenged the vaccine and said that people like me should apologize if he didn't die. He died shortly after getting his latest vaccine.

13. Yoho note: I knew Doug. No one ever accused him of being the smartest guy in the room. His death was attributed to Covid, and a complete autopsy was not performed.

14. **The Died Suddenly Facebook group** had over 300,000 members and was growing at 20,000 new people a day when Facebook removed it. This suggests a lot of people are dying suddenly all of a sudden. I wonder why?

15. **Polling done through independent polling companies** (using their lists) show people believe more people have been killed by the vaccines than by COVID. This would be impossible if the vaccines are perfectly safe. See Evidence of Harm.

16. **The unexplainably high number of people dropping dead in plain**

sight recently, and nobody even attempts to explain the cause or reveal the vaccination status of those who died.

17. **The book *Turtles all the way down: vaccine science and myth*** shows that the entire medical community has been fooled into believing that all vaccines are safe and effective. If it can happen for decades for all vaccines, it's not much of a stretch to believe it is happening with the COVID vaccines as well. There is a reward of $1K for anyone finding a mistake in the book. So far, no takers.

18. **Embalmer statistics**. Even today, around 60% or more of the cases have strange clots associated with the COVID vaccine.

19. **Insurance company data**. There was a 12 sigma increase in the number of deaths in people under 60 in Q3 and Q4 of 2021. This corresponds to the peak of vaccination in April (there is a 5 month delay from peak vaccination to peak death).

20. **The McCullough assumption.** If a healthy person suddenly dies, and there's no antecedent disease, *it's the vaccine until proven otherwise.*" (See Two top cardiologists implicate COVID vax in all unexplained heart attacks since 2021).

21. **Ignoring doctors who point out troubling safety statistics.** Dr. William Makis has pointed out 80 doctors in Canada who died of suspicious circumstances in close

time proximity to the COVID jabs. He wrote a letter to the CMA pointing this out and calling for an investigation. He was ignored. This should be extremely troubling to all doctors in Canada.

22. **Extreme anecdotes.** Stories like 6 stents, Wayne Root's wedding, my survey of over 600 people confirming Root's statistics, the podiatrist statistics, etc.

23. The Pfizer Phase 3 trial had more deaths in the vaccine group. The deaths were never properly investigated. Pfizer won't comment.

24. **Independent validation.** Dr. Naomi Wolf's team independently validated my claims on Fox News of hundreds of thousands killed and millions injured.

25. **UK data scientist Joel Smalley hasn't found any data supporting the safety of the COVID vaccines yet.** He's been looking worldwide since the start of the vaccination program for positive news on vaccine safety and hasn't found anything yet.

26. **The people in charge keep getting it wrong.** Surprisingly, we don't trust the people who accurately predicted what has happened and continue to trust the people who got it wrong.

27. **It's been over 18 months, and I still haven't found a single person willing to explain how any of this data (such as the items listed in Evidence of**

Harm) is consistent with a perfectly safe and effective vaccine. That should make anyone suspicious.

28. **Prominent people who once promoted the vaccine as safe and effective now realize that their original beliefs were based on trust and are calling for an immediate halt to the vaccines**. When they look directly at the evidence, they find that their trust was misplaced. Dr. Aseem Malhotra is the latest high-profile doctor to realize this, and nobody wants to debate him either.

29. **Other countries are admitting their mistakes.** Denmark is now not vaccinating anyone under 50 years old.

30. **Top doctors are calling for an end to booster mandates in universities in published papers.** They are being called unethical because the cure is worse than the disease. Amazingly, there has been no discussion on college campuses since that paper came out. For example, at Stanford, there is complete silence with no debate.

31. **A recent poll done in Australia showed huge dissatisfaction with the COVID vaccines.** An Australian poll of 45,000 respondents showed that only 35% of the vaccinated would get the shot again. Not a single unvaccinated person said they regretted the decision (there were 35% unvaccinated). So

only 22% of those surveyed are moving forward with future shots. The mainstream media doesn't acknowledge the poll.

32. **I hear stories all the time about doctors who privately tell people that they are worried by what they are seeing but keep quiet to save their jobs.** There is one in the comments of this article. If the vaccine is safe and effective, what's the explanation for this?

Still think I got it wrong?

Any doctor who thinks all of the above is just misinformation should join a vaccine injury support group and spend some time getting to know the vaccine injured and hear their stories. Here are links to groups that haven't been shut down yet that will welcome you:

Vaccine Injury/Side Effects Support Group (Facebook)

Covid Vaccine Injury Support Group (Trial Site News)

Summary

I have yet to find anyone who claims that I'm wrong about the COVID vaccines and is willing to sit down with me or any of my misinformation spreader colleagues to go through any of the data and show how it is consistent with the "safe and effective" narrative. They all decline.

I fail to understand how declining to engage in a discussion will save lives, but none of the people who decline will explain that.

More than two years ago, UCSF Professor Vinay Prasad co-authored a superb op-ed entitled, "Scientists who express different views on Covid-19 should be heard, not demonized."

Cassandra's Memo

Perhaps someone has written an opposing op-ed that argues convincingly that Vinay was wrong and that scientists who express different views should be demonized and not heard?

Chapter 16
Diversion: I Acted Like a Fool

I apologized but later retracted my apology.

I was with Liam, a modern 27-year-old man who is my son's best friend. To get to know him, I asked how he got accepted to his Ivy League university. My son was admitted there because he was an All-American runner, but Liam was initially too modest to tell me his own story.

SUBSTACK LINK

As I explored further, I learned that my young house-guest was a pianist, a concert viola player, a studious, competitive chess player, and a varsity runner and swimmer at Trinity, his elite prep school. He told me humbly that the place was filled with entitled brats whose parents were investment banker thieves. I had to press him to learn that he only missed one question when he took the SAT for admission to Brown University. He took it only once and did not study beforehand—a one-in-a-thousand result. At that point, I asked my wife if she understood how elite this kid was.

I thought that was more than enough, but then we started chatting about Liam's family. His siblings have degrees from Harvard, Oxford, and Cambridge and international research grants. His loving parents, who hosted my son like one of their own—for weeks at a time— own a well-known international book business they built over the past 20 years from scratch. Mama bear, who I have never met, sounds like a polymath. After I learned all this, I told my young friend that UCLA law school would not be a challenge for him.

By then, I felt Liam could have been one of my own, so I asked him if he had the jab. He said he had three, and I stopped, stunned.

I asked him if he realized that he had consented to injection with a toxin that potentially turned his body into a spike protein factory that might run for years—or the rest of his life, however short or long that might be. I discussed the Watson/Crick Nobel Prize-winning sequence of DNA to RNA to protein and how this is reversed and perverted by the mRNA injection. He did not know.

He had heard about the dying athletes and airline pilots and had family acquaintances who had also fallen after the jab. I told him about my friends dropping dead and my dear lifelong climbing partner who had a massive stroke and will never speak again. I asked Liam if he knew of the 85 percent plus miscarriage rate for pregnant women or the stunning 10 to 30 percent decrease in live births reported a few weeks ago in heavily "vaccinated" countries or if he understood that the chances against this happening by chance was trillions to one. He did not know.

I asked him if he understood the evidence proving the Gates foundation's or Fauci's guilt or the chain of evidence implicating the Chinese Communist Party in the Covid disaster. I asked if he knew Pfizer and Moderna were significantly (? majority) Chinese-owned. He did not know.

I wondered if he had considered the VAERS fatality data that, when extrapolated, showed tens of thousands of US deaths due to this Covid shot? Or that any vaccine before this had been discarded after less than 50 fatalities? Did he know that the German and Illinois insurance statistics showed the *entire population* had a forty (40) percent mortality increase coincident with the vax usage? Or that little children had a twenty (20) point IQ drop during the lockdowns? He had no idea.

I paused, and Liam assured me that his ethnic group was trained to sort out the truth using heated debate and that discussions like this were expected in his family. So I went on in this vein for another twenty minutes.

He did not know about the court-ordered Pfizer/FDA document dump or the analysis showing they knew two months after the rollout that their product would kill thousands, possibly millions, worldwide. He did not realize that Pfizer tried to get the court to release the material over *seventy-five* (75) years, an undeniable badge of fraud.

I discussed the other lies surrounding Covid and the jab. That treatments such as ivermectin would have saved millions of human lives but were concealed behind a wall of coordinated propaganda. Did he remember the horse medication ads? Did he realize that the Covid "long hauler" syndrome and the Sudden Adult Death Syndrome (SADS) were virtually all vax injuries and not mysteries? That Sudden Infant Death Syndrome (SIDS) nearly always occurs within a week after childhood vaccines? That no pediatric vaccines had been studied using placebo controls? (These will never be properly studied because vaccines were granted relief from civil liability in 1986.)

Liam asked weakly whether these examples might be a correlation and not causation. So I asked him whether he knew that more than 10,000 normal US children had fallen to the floor immediately after a childhood vaccination, began banging their heads, and *never spoke again*? Did he understand that childhood "autism"—neurological damage —had gone from less than 1/10,000 to 1/30 since Congress granted the vaccine liability relief in 1986? Or that the number of vaccine injections recommended by "authorities" was five when I was a kid and seventy-five (75)* now? Or that the incidences of the diseases the vaccines were purported to prevent were ALL dropping like stones due to simple public health measures *before the vaxes were introduced?* These damning "anecdotes" made further study or usage of these injections a criminal act. *This was before approval of the yearly Covid shot for minors.

Did he now understand that these fake "diseases" were gaslighting? That well, after this, I went speechless. He hadn't heard any of it before.

Relations between sons and fathers are fraught. My son and I always circle each other like dogs, observing and sniffing warily. We love each other, but he would never put up with a beating such as I laid on his friend. Our relationship is freighted with our history.

But Liam and I have no such handicap. He may have seen me as an old fool that he had to suffer, but I doubt it. To his credit, he listened. The advantage of being twice someone's age is the ability to read their mind. I am sure I showed him enough of the matrix that he saw its outlines.

Current events are so complex that for those with little information—and that's almost everyone now because most sources have been kidnapped—reading *The Real Anthony Fauci* and other references is the only path to the truth. The hardest part to grok is the profound evil of the actors behind the plots. Some of them care more about torturing us than acquiring a fortune, which is incomprehensible.

Liam is the smartest guy in almost any room, even in my home. He had already worked through the start of *Butchered by "Healthcare,"* so he reads. I am hoping that Liam gets the memo now. We need lawyers with his talents, and he had better not get any more injections if he doesn't want to *drop dead.*

I also hope—even pray—that my son listens to him. He doesn't listen much to me.

Cassandra's Memo

Lucky from Tobago loves garbage and refuses dog food. If you dine on social media, you are just like him.

Part Four

Hospitals Have Become
Contract Killers

Chapter 17
Hospitals Are Openly Bribed to Mistreat Covid Patients

My daughter Grace and many others were murdered by doctors and nurses who prioritized their paychecks over the Hippocratic Oath. These people are the pawns in a global agenda that is too evil for most to comprehend.

— Scott Schara

Because I spent my formative years training in hospitals, stories like the following shock and horrify me more than the others. Each time I review them, I doubt the reality that we are living through.

During the early months of the pandemic, the planners forbade elective surgeries for many months. This was purportedly done to limit Covid transmission, but it did not affect the pandemic and cost hospitals tens to possibly hundreds of billions of dollars. To supposedly compensate these institutions for their lost revenue, the federal government instituted bonuses for each Covid case treated.

This inflated case numbers and hospitalizations. These

were widely publicized, which raised anxiety levels. Because the federally approved treatments were so toxic, a massive increase in complications and deaths ensued, along with a second round of news coverage and panic.

Here is how the system (still) works. Everyone who enters a hospital for admission or outpatient surgery is coerced into getting a Covid "PCR" test. The inventor of this technology, Kary Mullis, received the Nobel prize, but he said the test should never be used to diagnose disease because it causes massive overdiagnosis. This happened— more than 90 percent of recent "cases" are false positives. These people are not sick and have no symptoms that would confirm their condition.

Currently, about 40 percent of all people visiting US emergency rooms for any cause have a positive Covid test. For those who test positive and are then admitted, a 20 percent bonus—or more—is paid on all hospital charges in addition to the usual fees. This promotes universal testing and then the use of the most expensive treatments regardless of their toxicity.

For example, soon after the first cases were treated, intubation with mechanical breathing was determined to be the wrong approach for Covid because it kills more people than it saves. But intubated patients require treatment in intensive care units, which adds thousands of dollars a day to the bill and qualifies for the bonus.

For decades, treating facilities have received a 20 percent "administration fee" or kickback from drug companies when their medications are administered in clinics or hospitals. (I wrote about this in Butchered by "Healthcare.") During Covid, bonuses of up to 65 percent have been instituted for certain bills. The extra hospital reimbursement can be hundreds of thousands of dollars per patient in addition to the usual exorbitant fees.

Remdesivir, a failed Ebola treatment, is pressed on patients even though it has no therapeutic effects and kills a third to half of the people who receive it. Patients get so sick that they are often hospitalized for weeks and may end up in intensive care. Remdesivir retails for thousands of dollars for a five to ten-day course, and hospitals get a bonus for using it.

Hospital doctors cooperating with their institutions may diagnose Covid retrospectively—*after the patient dies*— based on the clinical picture, despite a negative PCR test. The hospital bonus is calculated, and the windfall is billed. Patient families may be persuaded to keep quiet about this because they receive up to $9000 to pay for their loved ones' funeral costs.

These incentives license patient butchery. The fraudulent PCR test over-diagnoses. Next, mortally dangerous interventions are performed instead of using $100 worth of ivermectin and nutraceuticals. The package can cost hundreds of thousands per person more than routine hospital costs—and frequently kills the patient. The system was designed to exaggerate the dangers of coronavirus and slaughter many of us to terrify the rest. Gaslighting about it all continues.

When you hear the podcasts below, you will suspect that there are also bonuses when patients die, but I have not been able to find documentation for this detail. Michael Yeadon says, "There is no question that the State deliberately put people on midazolam and morphine for the purpose of terminating their lives. Neither of those drugs would ever be appropriate in an open airway breathing patient. Midazolam and morphine repress their respiration.

The doses used were between 3-5X the recommended dose." (From Exposing the Darkness newsletter).

Sources

From the *Federal Register*, Additional Policy and Regulatory Revisions in Response to the COVID-19 Public Health Emergency:

> Centers for Medicare & Medicaid Services issued an Interim Final Rule with Comment Period that established the New COVID-19 Treatments Add-on Payment (NCTAP) under the Medicare Inpatient Prospective Payment System (IPPS). The NCTAP, designed to mitigate potential financial disincentives for hospitals to provide new COVID-19 treatments, is effective from November 2, 2020, until the end of the fiscal year in which the COVID-19 public health emergency (PHE) ends...
>
> For eligible cases, the NCTAP is equal to the lesser of these:
>
> 65% of the operating outlier threshold for the claim
>
> 65% of the amount by which the costs of the case exceed the standard Diagnosis-Related Group (DRG) payment (including the adjustment to the relative weight under Section 3710 of the Coronavirus Aid, Relief, and Economic Security Act (CARES Act)

More about the NCTAP HERE and HERE.
About the funeral expenses HERE.

* * *

HOW COULD all this be true?

This hospital behavior is not new. Although many people who work in hospitals are idealistic, most of these corporations are ruthless pirates that loot the patients who trust them. These companies pay or bully physicians into cooperating with their agendas. *Butchered by "Healthcare"* (2020) explains:

> *Market economists I've spoken with variously refer to hospitals as "sharks" or "spending machines." With few, if any, market forces to effectively curb their behavior, they raise prices as much as they can. Because most hospitals are nonprofit institutions, they have no shareholders to answer to and cannot legally show a "profit"; therefore, they spend excess income on executive compensation and building Zen gardens and marble lobbies.*
>
> Elisabeth Rosenthal, An American Sickness (2017)

Hospitals cause an epidemic of damage. Estimates for preventable deaths yearly in US hospitals range from 200,000 to over 400,000. As far back as 1998, a JAMA report estimated there were 100,000 deaths a year from hospital medication blunders alone. These are the tip of an iceberg of error, for most mistakes cause harm rather than death.

These institutions are enormously influential and wealthy. They gobble about a third of US healthcare spending, over a trillion dollars a year. Their supporters include doctors, drug companies, and thousands of employees. Local business leaders throw money their way with pricey donation dinners.

Cardiac or other specialty units often make the most for them. Profit margins for some, such as Ohio State, are over 30 percent.

Over 75 percent of all American hospitals, and eight of the ten largest, are nonprofit. Many were initially Catholic charities run by nuns, who worked for free. Now, the nonprofits operate almost identically to the for-profits but are less accountable because they have no shareholders or analysts watching them. They make money, and they call it an "operating surplus." The nonprofits and the for-profits spend about the same percentage of their revenue on charity, 5 percent or less.

Rather than declare surpluses or pay taxes with the money thrown to them, hospital systems typically build, market, buy equipment, and pay their executives bonuses. They also purchase physicians' practices. These instantly become more profitable because insurance collections improve when hospital "facility" billing codes are used. This can double or triple collections.

Some hospitals buy every healthcare facility in an entire region, then jack up the prices using their monopoly power. Insurance carriers are less effective in negotiating with these institutions because they may be the only choice in the area. (There is more.)

* * *

SCOTT SCHARA LEARNED about hospitals the hard way.

His daughter Grace was admitted for a positive Covid test. She was speaking and alert when her doctor signed a "Do Not Resuscitate" protocol. He did not discuss this with the family or ask for permission. Following this, he ordered the staff to give Grace three intravenous sedatives nearly simultaneously. No one could have lived through it.

Grace's doctors never offered any treatment known to

be effective for Covid. For the whole story, see ouramazing-grace.net.

Grace Schara

SUBSTACK LINK

* * *

ANOTHER MURDER: Robb Garmong's wife

I could hardly stand to do this interview and was tearful during part of it. Robb's precious wife Tasse had recovered from Covid but went to the emergency department several times with dehydration. When she was finally admitted, Robb was not allowed to accompany her because they said he was "contact traced Covid positive."

Even though his wife was alert and in no breathing distress, she was sedated, intubated, and given Remdesivir. The hospital people later claimed that she gave her consent. Robb says, "We know this is not true because she was against intubation and had warned numerous police detectives against it." Tasse was nearly dead when Robb was finally given permission to see her. The doctor ignored her husband's frantic efforts to speak with him.

SUBSTACK LINK The Rumble link is HERE.

Robb held his wife close for her last few hours and stayed by her bedside for an hour after she died.

Robb and Scott have filed malpractice suits, but the problems are systemic rather than doctor errors.

Other resources

- See Mercola's article in the next chapter. This has Covid treatment information at the end.
- This LINK at the Truth For Health Foundation explains this incentive plan. HERE is another.
- Many stories on the Children's Health Defense site explain this as well.
- Elizabeth Lee Vliet, MD, has other background information.
- Front Line Critical Care Alliance (FLCCC) has in-hospital treatment protocols that work. They avoid intubation and never use Remdesivir.

Postscript by Scott Schara

Numbers do not lie. The US has three times the land mass of India, 24% of its population, and over twice its deaths from COVID. We have the best medical facilities on the planet, only 4.3% of the world's population, and are the only country with over 1 million COVID deaths. Hospital protocols are to blame, for we are the only country using the following:

•Ventilators – 90% kill rate

•Remdesivir – 75% kill rate for three doses or more

•End-of-life sedation medications: Precedex, Lorazepam, Morphine

•"Do Not Resuscitate" orders without family or patient consent.

Why do the elderly and disabled population groups have the highest Covid mortality? In the first 22 months of Covid, $400 billion was paid to hospitals to enforce these death protocols. (source: Senator Ron Johnson's January 24, 2022, hearing). The annual Federal Budget is $5.6 trillion. The yearly Federal Budget for Medicare (elderly) and Medicaid (disabled) is $2.2 trillion, 39% of the total. The elderly and disabled are a financial burden to society. Grace was taken from us because of this agenda.

Chapter 18
Mercola: COVID Patients are Being Slaughtered in the Hospitals

Around the US, COVID-19 patients are being killed by inappropriate medical protocols, and most have no choice about their treatment.

— Joseph Mercola

B y Joseph Mercola, February 16, 2022, read by Robert Yoho, MD (ret). Scan this article to confirm the nearly unbelievable story in the last chapter.

STORY AT-A-GLANCE

COVID patients may be denied basic drugs like antibiotics and steroids. They are sometimes not even given nutrition and fluids, which is a crime during wartime. These patients are instead frequently treated with remdesivir, narcotics, and mechanical ventilation, which can be fatal.

Hospitals are given cash by the federal

141

government for COVID testing, COVID diagnoses, and COVID hospital admissions. They
are also rewarded separately for prescribing
remdesivir, mechanical ventilation, and even
for the fatalities.

The Canadian press reports that COVID-
19 patients are often given excessive doses of
medications such as opioids, benzodiazepines, and anticholinergics. These may be
lethal. And in the U.K., nursing homes have
been accused of killing COVID patients using
midazolam, a powerful sedative.

Patient neglect, mistreatment, overtreatment, and the COVID jabs have resulted in
massive disability and death. Deaths among
working-age Americans (18 to 64) in the third
quarter of 2021 were 40% higher than the
prepandemic rates. Compare that to the
15.4% increase seen between 2019 and 2020,
which was reported as the highest life insurance payout increase in 100 years

SUBSTACK LINK

The unthinkable is happening in America's hospitals.

COVID-19 patients have little say-so in the treatment they receive and some are dying because of inappropriate protocols. They have been stripped of their patient rights.

Some are refused basic drugs like antibiotics and steroids, and sometimes nutrition and fluid are being denied. The Geneva Convention states that even prisoners of war must be provided necessities such as food.

COVID patients are instead frequently over-treated with dangerous and ineffective therapies such as remdesivir, narcotics, and mechanical ventilation. This combination often results in death.

Medical kidnapping for profit. Benjamin Gord was a perfectly healthy man who was in a car accident. He claims he was given an unknown knock-out drug by a paramedic and woke up on life support in a COVID ward.

He was unharmed from the accident, so he yanked out the breathing tube by himself. When he demanded to know why he'd been placed on mechanical ventilation, the staff told him he was being treated for COVID.

In other cases, patients have been given COVID care like this even though they came in for something else and have no COVID symptoms. Many are also being denied hospital release and so are almost held as prisoners. Many are unable to refuse treatment.

Some COVID patients are forced to accept inappropriate do-not-resuscitate orders. Others are given potent sedative combinations such as morphine, fentanyl, and midazolam. Doctors call these "euthanasia cocktails."

This medical kidnapping and mistreatment of patients against their will has become widespread. Human rights attorney Thomas Renz asked the Truth for Health Foundation to set up the "COVID Care Strategy Team" to help families take their loved ones out of hospitals where they are being held captive.4

Federal payments incentivize patient deaths.
How could this have happened? Hospitals are receiving money to over-treat COVID patients, and they sometimes die. Here are their incentives:5,6

• Bonus for COVID testing and COVID diagnoses — Hospitals receive a 20% "bonus" in addition to standard hospital fees if they treat a COVID patient7

• Bonus for admission of anyone diagnosed as a COVID patient

• Bonus for use of remdesivir — The U.S. government pays hospitals a bonus when they use remde-sivir.8,9,10 This is in addition to the routine 20 percent bonus that pharma companies pay for drugs used in hospitals.

Remdesivir was tested for Ebola in 2014, but it didn't work and caused many fatalities. In early 2020, testing was begun for COVID.11 Life-threatening side effects were found including kidney failure and liver damage.15 Despite the hazards and ineffectiveness, the FDA authorized remde-sivir for emergency use against COVID in May 2020.16 Full approval was granted in October 2020.17

• Bonus for mechanical ventilation. This kills 84.9% of COVID patients within as few as 96 hours according to whistleblowers.

• Bonus for COVID deaths — In August 2020, former director of the U.S. Centers for Disease Control and Prevention, Robert Redfield, confirmed that hospitals had a financial incentive to overcount COVID deaths.20

Patients effectively have a bounty on their heads. According to Renz, hospitals receive a minimum of $100,000 extra for each COVID patient if they use remdesivir and ventilation. The hospitals that refuse to obey this protocol and use drugs such as ivermectin, antibiotics, and steroids forfeit the extra payments.

At the start of the pandemic, hospitals were losing revenue from routine care and elective surgeries that had declined.21 So these COVID incentives were initially justified as a way to make sure that hospitals would not be financially penalized. But the payment scheme has created a kind of institutionalized killing machine. Hospital revenue is now tied to patients dying in-hospital with a COVID label, whether it is true or false.

COVID Patients are over-drugged. Other countries are reporting similar trends. The Canadian Press reports that COVID-19 patients are often given excessive doses of medications such as opioids, benzodiazepines, and anticholinergics that can be lethal.22

In the U.K., senior care homes have been accused of killing off COVID patients with midazolam, a powerful sedative. In April 2020, 38,352 out-of-hospital prescriptions for midazolam were issued, while the monthly average for the prior five years was only 15,000.

Retired neurologist Dr. Patrick Pullicino told MailOnline,23 "Midazolam depresses respiration and it hastens death. It changes end-of-life care into euthanasia,"

At the end of 2021, the government of New Zealand approved "voluntary euthanasia" for COVID patients by lethal injection if the doctor believed that they were unlikely to recover.24 The doctor who performs the euthanasia gets paid $1,087 by the government.25

Hospital incentives are deadly. The new focus in hospitals seems to be maximizing the death toll rather than saving lives. The COVID jabs are touted as the only way forward despite data from the U.S. Department of

Defense that suggests these are causing unprecedented injuries and deaths. The Defense Medical Epidemiology Database (DMED) data was obtained by attorney Thomas Renz from DOD whistleblowers and was released on his website.26 He says that the numbers prove that the vaccines are injuring and sometimes killing the military. The public, however, still believes the marketing claiming they are "safe and effective."

Compared to the previous five-year averages, miscarriages were up 279% among DOD personnel in 2021, breast cancer was up 487%, nervous system disorders 1,048%, male infertility 350%, female infertility 471%, ovarian dysfunction 437%, and on and on. As noted by Renz during U.S. Sen. Ron Johnson's "COVID-19: A Second Opinion" panel:27

The Whistleblower data, this DMED database, has provided a control group of sorts. Its military records dating back several years supply medical codes for various medical issues that our military personnel face such as cancers, miscarriages, neurological disorders, and so on.

These records were provided by three military doctors (and)... show a historical baseline of what the health of the American military was like before 2021, the year the COVID vaccine was released. What you see is quite disturbing.

From 2016 to 2020 medical conditions show little variation. But in 2021, when the vaccine was mandated, there was a spike in cancers, miscarriages, infertility, and other diseases. The increase was by factors of hundreds to thousands of percent.

These vaccines are injuring and sometimes killing our military, and the public still believes the marketing that they are "safe and effective."

The Pentagon immediately claimed that there was a "glitch" in their database. They said that the true numbers of diseases in the five years Renz was using as a baseline were far higher. If they were not lying to cover up the disaster, 2021 would look more typical.

Maj. Charlie Dietz, a task force public affairs officer for the DOD, claimed that DMED was taken offline "to identify and correct the root cause of the data corruption." Once the supposed "missing" medical diagnoses were added back in, the reported number of diseases and injuries for 2021 was 3% LOWER than 2020. That would give 2021 the lowest numbers in six years. As reported by The Blaze:28

Where those true numbers existed, why they weren't in the system for five years, what exactly was in the system, and why the 2021 numbers were accurate according to the DOD account remain a mystery.

However, one by one, the military public health officials have been adding back random numbers to the 2016 through 2020 codes. I'm told by Renz and two of the whistleblowers that throughout the past week, they have queried the same data again, and in most of the ICD categories, they have found that the numbers from 2016 through 2020 were 'increased' exponentially make 2021 look normal.

This has been done without any transparency, any press release, any statement of narrative, and sloppily. Their already unbelievable narrative is now entirely ridiculous.

In addition to believing that every epidemiological report for five years was somehow completely tainted with false data ... we would have to believe that the minute they discovered this from Renz, they suddenly discovered the exact numbers. A five-year mistake fixed overnight!

Incompetence, corruption, both — or worse?

Making this clown-show even more indefensible is that the Centers for Disease Control and Prevention's Advisory Committee on Immunization Practices (ACIP) has admitted that they've been monitoring the DMED data from the start.29

If the DoD just now discovered corrupted data in the DMED, then there's incompetence in its ranks. And if ACIP was looking at the DMED data and kept pushing for vaccination despite alarming safety signals, then ACIP is criminally negligent.

If there's nothing wrong with the database and the numbers Renz initially obtained were accurate, then people within the DOD are falsifying data to cover up COVID jab injuries and sacrificing our military to protect Big Pharma. If this happened, it could be interpreted as treason.

As noted by Steve Kirsch,30 founder of the COVID-19 Early Treatment Fund, the DOD's "explanation" for the discrepancy in its 2021 military injury statistics is riddled with holes. For example, they have never explained why the 2016 through 2020 data were affected, yet 2021 was not.

Secondly, they've not explained how they were able to correct "underreporting" of health problems from 2016 through 2020. How did they know there was underreporting? And why didn't they fix it earlier? Thirdly, and perhaps most importantly, Kirsch concludes,

Only symptoms that were elevated by the vaccine were affected; a computer glitch can't have caused that ... That makes their 'corruption' explanation hard to explain. Very hard to explain.

Pfizer warns investors. In its fourth-quarter earnings release and risk disclosure,31,32 the company admits that "the possibility of unfavorable new preclinical, clinical or safety data... including by audit or inspection" could impact earnings. They also note the decline in public confidence, concerns about data integrity, and prescriber and pharmacy education as potential risks. They also acknowledge that COVID-19 might "diminish in severity or prevalence, or disappear entirely."

All-cause deaths soared in 2021. Patient neglect, mistreatment, overtreatment, and the COVID jabs have resulted in massive disability and death. In early January 2022, OneAmerica, a national mutual life insurance company based in Indianapolis, reported that deaths among working-age Americans (18 to 64) as of the third quarter of 2021 were 40% higher than prepandemic rates — and they are not dying from COVID. In December 2021, Fortune magazine reported this as the highest life insurance payout increase in 100 years.33 Scott Davidson, the CEO of OneAmerica, said:34

> We are seeing, right now, the highest death rates we have seen in the history of this business — and not just at OneAmerica. The data is consistent across every player in our business.
>
> And what we saw in just the third quarter, we're seeing it continue into the fourth quarter, is that death rates are up 40% over what they were pre-pandemic. To give you an idea of how bad that is, a three-sigma or a one-in-200-year catastrophe would be a 10% increase over pre-pandemic. So, 40% is just unheard of."

OneAmerica has simultaneously noticed an increase in disability claims. Initially, there was a rise in short-term claims, but now most claims are for long-term disabilities. The company expects the increase in claims to cost them well over $100 million, an unexpected expense that will be passed on to employers who buy group life insurance policies.

The global life insurance industry had claims of $5.5 billion in the first nine months of 2021. This was when the COVID jabs were being aggressively rolled out. But during all of 2020, the height of the pandemic, the claims were only $3.5 billion.35 According to one insurance broker cited by Reuters, the industry was caught off-guard, because they thought the mass vaccination campaign would result in lower payouts in 2021. Reuters also reports that:36

· The Dutch insurer Aegon, which does two-thirds of its business in the U.S., saw U.S. claims rise from $31 million in 2020, to $111 million in 2021.

· U.S. insurers MetLife and Prudential Financial also reported an increase in claims for 2021 compared to 2020 and the prepandemic years.

· Reinsurer Munich Re raised its 2021 estimate of COVID-19 life and health claims from 400 million euros to 600 million euros.

If COVID is treated immediately and aggressively as an outpatient, it is typically just an ordinary flu. This is not the time to go to the hospital unless your life depends on it. You cannot count on them to treat you properly as you could in the past. If you trust them, you could end up dead.

Your best alternative is to be prepared. Create a "COVID survival kit," much like you would a tornado or hurricane kit, so you can treat yourself at first symptoms. Perhaps you just have a common cold or regular influenza; maybe it's the much milder Omicron, but it's hard to tell them apart. You must treat all cold/flu symptoms just like you would treat early COVID.

Remember, this applies to those who have gotten the jab as well since this does not prevent infection. It may make you even more vulnerable.

Effective treatment protocols include:

- The Front Line COVID-19 Critical Care Alliance's (FLCCC's) prevention and early at-home treatment protocol. They also have an in-hospital protocol and long-term management guidance for long-haul COVID-19 syndrome. You can find a listing of doctors who can prescribe ivermectin and other necessary medicines on the FLCCC website
- The AAPS protocol
- Tess Lawrie's World Council for Health protocol
- America's Frontline Doctors

Chapter 19
Sophisticated Advanced Directive

U sing this document or one like it may help you to avoid some of the ill deeds that hospital doctors perpetrated on Rob Garmong's wife, Scott Schara's daughter, and thousands more. Be sure that providers acknowledge receipt in writing. Write down their names. Notarization is nice but may not be necessary.

* * *

I, _____, residing at
_____ make, constitute and appoint
_____, residing at
_____ (hereinafter referred to as my "Health Care Representative"), my true and lawful attorney-in-fact to be my Health Care Representative with respect to all health care matters except the specific provisions following, upon the terms and conditions hereinafter set forth.

1. IN NO CASE shall a vaccine of any kind--Covid, influenza, or any other--be administered to

_____. And in NO CASE shall Remdesivir be administered to _____. And in NO CASE shall sedation, intubation, and mechanical ventilation for Covid treatment be undertaken unless the health care representative agrees and consents IN WRITING. And in NO CASE shall _____ be considered for hospice or end-of-life care unless the health care representative agrees and consents IN WRITING.

2A. IF TRANSFUSION IS RECOMMENDED BY PHYSICIAN PERSONNEL, it will NOT be permitted under any circumstances unless either of the following criteria are met:

1) The blood is obtained from a donor of the Healthcare Representative's choice, or:

2) My situation is life-threatening, my hemoglobin level is below 5 a/dL, and all other options have been exhausted. These include volume expanders (saline, dextran. Haemaccel. Rinaer's lactate solution. Hydroxvethvl starch HAS) or similar, iron preparations (intramuscular or intravenous), artificially prepared ESF, or suctioning the blood from the wound and returning it to the circulation (Autotransfusion ATS/MAT or Retransfusion ADR).

The Healthcare Representative must be consulted for any consideration of blood transfusion and will have the final decision authority. The Representative has been directed to REFUSE any transfusion unless she agrees to it IN WRITING before it happens.

2B. Routine maintenance intravenous hydration is permitted at replacement levels of one (1) milliliter per kilogram of body weight per hour. For fluid given in excess of this guideline, documentation of the reasons why must be written into the patient notes and cosigned by the Healthcare representative before the excess is given. The Healthcare representative may elect to grant written permission for a trusted doctor to manage this instead of her.

3. The Healthcare Representative will at all times have ABSOLUTE POWER to discharge _____ from the hospital against medical advice under any circumstances whatsoever. Interference will be considered battery.

4. I desire that my wishes concerning all health care matters be carried out through the authority given to my Health Care Representative under this Health Care Power of Attorney despite any contrary feelings, beliefs, or opinions of doctors, other family members, relatives, or friends. I have thoroughly discussed my personal preferences and desires with my Health Care Representative and their successor. I am fully satisfied that each will know best what I would wish, and I have the utmost faith and confidence in their respective sound judgments.

In exercising the authority herein given to my Health Care Representative, my Health Care Representative should discuss with me the specifics of any proposed health care decision if I can communicate in any manner whatsoever, even by blinking my eyes. I hereby further direct and instruct my Health Care Representative that if I am unable to give informed consent to my medical treatment or if the physician(s) providing me with medical care determine that I cannot make a particular health care decision, my Health Care Representative shall make such health care decision for me based upon any treatment choices or other desires that I have previously expressed while competent, whether under this Health Care Power of Attorney or otherwise.

My Health Care Representative is authorized to do any one or more of the following:

(i) To sign on my behalf any documents necessary to carry out the authorizations described below, including waivers or releases of liabilities required by any healthcare provider;

(ii) To give or withhold consent to any medical care or treatment, to revoke or change any consent previously given or implied by law for any medical care or treatment, and to arrange for my placement in or removal from any hospital, convalescent home or other health care institution;

5. The rights and authority conferred on my Health Care Representative herein appointed shall include, but is by no means limited to, the right to receive information and reports from all treating physicians, other healthcare professionals, healthcare institutions, etc., regarding proposed health care, surgery, or any other aspect of my medical treatment. It shall include the right to receive and review my medical records and information to the same extent that I am entitled to and to disclose or consent to the disclosure of my medical records to others. It shall include the ability to contract on my behalf for any healthcare-related service or facility (without my Health Care Representative incurring personal financial liability for such contracts); and to hire and fire physicians, social services, and other support personnel responsible for my care.

6. This instrument is to be construed and interpreted as an "advance directive for health care" as such a term is defined in California statute. In determining the rights of my Health Care Representative herein appointed, the enumeration of the specific items, rights, acts, or powers set forth herein is not intended to nor does it limit, and it is not to be construed or interpreted as limiting, the specific power of my Health Care Representative to do and perform any and all acts with respect to my health care that I would be able to perform if I were competent and able to do so and as are within the bounds of authority granted by the Act.

7. In the event _____ shall become
unable to act as my Health Care Representative here-
under for any reason whatsoever, including, but not
limited to, death, incapacity, or resignation, then I do
hereby make, constitute and appoint
_____ as successor Health Care Repre-
sentative to serve in the place of the Health Care Representative first above named.

8. No person who relies in good faith upon any representations by my Health Care Representative or any
successor Health Care Representative shall be liable to me,
my estate, my heirs or my assigns, for recognizing the
Health Care Representative's authority. The directions of
my Health Care Representative shall be binding in all
respects upon all those involved in my care. My Health
Care Representative and all those acting upon his or her
directions shall be entitled to indemnification from my
estate in connection with all claims asserted against them,
unless the directions given and relied on are wholly incon-
sistent with my intentions as expressed above.

9. If a guardian of my person should for any reason be
appointed, I hereby nominate my Health Care Representative _____ and as alternate,
_____ named above.

10. ADMINISTRATIVE PROVISIONS

(A) I hereby revoke any prior Health Care Power of
Attorney.

(B) This Health Care Power of Attorney is intended to
be valid in any jurisdiction in which it is presented.

(C) My Health Care Representative shall not be entitled to compensation for services performed under this
Health Care Power of Attorney, but he or she shall be entitled to reimbursement for all reasonable expenses incurred

as a result of carrying out any provisions of this Health Care Power of Attorney.

(D) In the event of any disagreement between my Health Care Representative and my attending physician concerning my decision-making capacity or the appropriate interpretation and application of the terms of this Health Care Power of Attorney to my course of treatment, it is my wish and desire that such disagreement is resolved by the written direction of my Health Care Representative.

(E) The powers delegated under this Health Care Power of Attorney are separate so that the invalidity of any one (1) or more powers shall not affect any others.

11. By this instrument, I intend to create a durable power of attorney effective upon and only during any period of incapacity in which, in the opinion of (i) my Health Care Representative and (ii) one or more confirming physicians, I lack capacity to make a particular health care decision (i.e. "Period of Incapacity"). The rights, powers, and authority of my Health Care Representative herein appointed shall commence and shall be in full force and effect upon any such determination as to the commencement of a Period of Incapacity, and such rights, powers, and authority shall remain in full force and effect from the above-mentioned date until such time as I have regained my capacity to make such health care decision(s) or until my death, as the case may be; PROVIDED, HOWEVER, that this Health Care Power of Attorney may be revoked by me by a written instrument duly acknowledged before a notary public or by such other manner as shall be allowed under the Act; and PROVIDED, FURTHER, that my regaining capacity following any Period of Incapacity shall not be treated as an event causing the revocation of this Health Care Power

of Attorney and this Health Care Power of Attorney shall be construed as if such Period of Incapacity never occurred.

I UNDERSTAND THE PURPOSE AND EFFECT OF THIS HEALTH CARE POWER OF ATTORNEY AND SIGN IT AFTER CAREFUL DELIBERATION THIS _____ DAY OF _____, 20___.

Each of the undersigned declares that the person who signed this Health Care Power of Attorney did so in the presence of the undersigned; that said person is personally known to the undersigned and appears to be of sound mind and acting willingly and free from duress or undue influence; and that each of the undersigned and the person executing this Health Care Power of Attorney is 18 years of age or older; and the undersigned is not designated as the person's Health Care Representative under this Health Care Power of Attorney.

_____ residing at

_____

STATE OF CALIFORNIA SS: COUNTY OF LOS ANGELES

_____ residing at

_____

STATE OF CALIFORNIA SS: COUNTY OF LOS ANGELES

I hereby certify that on [date]

_____ personally came before me and acknowledged under oath, to my satisfaction, that [he/she] is the person named in and personally signed this Health Care Power of Attorney, and that [he/she] signed, sealed and delivered this Health Care Power of Attorney as [his/her] act and deed for the uses and purposes therein expressed.

* * *

Notes

Even if you use this document or another like it, you should still stay at the bedside during the hospitalization of loved ones. Watch everyone carefully.

So many false positives happen with the Covid tests that many are admitted to the hospital for something else and find themselves falsely diagnosed with Covid and treated with hazardous therapies.

Transfusion of blood from vaccinated people can cause "long hauler's" syndrome, but if you have had significant blood loss, you may be forced to accept any blood you can get. Reports about these problems are HERE and HERE and HERE. Pierre Kory is treating one of my readers for this issue.

My blood transfusion criteria above may be too conservative if you are old or frail and need a transfusion to save your life. Learn about the issues and make your own decision. Think ahead and get advice, for it may be too late to figure it out later.

THIS is a summary of how to obtain or donate untainted blood. I had a reader write me that a Red Cross blood bank was refusing to accept blood from "boosted" individuals because it was too "thick," but most branches refuse to recognize any problem.

Remdesivir is a dangerous, ineffective drug that causes fatalities in a quarter to half of the patients. Fauci hustled it through the approval process. It should never be used.

Hospital personnel have recently been occasionally

guilty of killing patients by giving them too much intravenous fluid. Watching for this may require nursing knowledge. Clause 2B in this document puts providers on notice
that they are being observed.

Although hospice care may be helpful for some, do not
call them unless you have decided to die. Some plans receive
a lump sum of money for all your treatments, so their daily
pay is better if you die earlier. This conflict of interest can get
you poisoned—be sure that is what you want. If you get
involved with these people, watch them carefully.

Given what we know, every vaccine does more harm
than good, and all should be taken off the market. Para-
phrasing Toby Rogers, the Covid jab is beyond ridiculous.

Finally, if your care providers seem resistant to these
ideas, or—worse—if you sense hostility, consider leaving
against medical advice or switching facilities if you can.
Always be polite and respectful, but consider bringing an
attorney or local sheriff to the hospital to discharge your loved
ones.

"LEGAL" DISCLAIMER: This is for informational
purposes only. Use it at your own risk. Check it with an
attorney and doctor whom you trust and modify it as they
direct and your best judgment advises you. I am retired and
neither practice law nor medicine.

Chapter 20
Diversion: I Travel to Exotic Places

I used an airport ad to fake this beach selfie.

Part Five

Every Vaccine Kills More People Than It Saves

Chapter 21
What the Childhood Vaccine Schedule Looks Like

For ourselves, we shall not trouble you with specious
pretenses... and make a long speech that would not be
believed... You know as well as we do that right, as the
world goes, is only in question between equals in power,
while the strong do what they can and the weak suffer
what they must.

> — Thucydides, The History of the
> Peloponnesian War

About 75 individual shots are now on the
recommended vaccination schedule, not
including the recently added yearly Covid vax. I
am 69, and there were only five jabs when I was a baby.

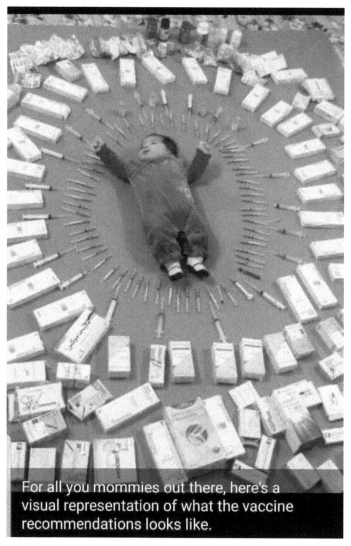

For all you mommies out there, here's a visual representation of what the vaccine recommendations looks like.

Source: 2nd Smartest Guy in the World HERE. Originally published November 4, 2022.

Although this image alone is persuasive, the rest of this section presents comprehensive proof that all vaccines are expensive, catastrophic failures. Since the drug industry's vaccine liability was limited in 1986, they have been using this class of drugs to replace others as the supposed solution for health concerns. For example, vaccines are now being developed for cholesterol, and mRNA technology is being used for the influenza vaccine. It is a new healthcare model.

The FDA recently approved the toxic Covid vaccine for yearly childhood use—eighteen more jabs in addition to the above. This lack of regulation, lawsuit immunity, and government support produce incredible profits. These have been impossible for the companies to resist even as it becomes clear that their drugs are killing people.

Corporate representatives claim that studying vaccines is unethical because "the science proves they work." But no vaccine has ever been compared to a sugar pill or saline control, and all have serious side effects.

Chapter 22
The Final Word on Childhood Vaccines From Three Authors

I AM AN abolitionist.
By Toby Rogers, Sep 16, 2022

SUBSTACK LINK

I The best vaccine data set in the world

The Bandim Health Project (BHP) in Guinea-Bissau (west Africa) has the best data set in the world on vaccine benefits and harms. Founded in 1978 by the legendary Danish doctor and anthropologist Peter Aaby, the Bandim Health Project is a collaboration between the Ministry of

Public Health in Guinea-Bissau, the Statens Serum Institut in Denmark, and researchers affiliated with the University of Southern Denmark and Aarhus University. BHP monitors and studies the health of more than 200,000 people in urban and rural Guinea-Bissau. They have datasets going back decades that enable them to measure long-term health outcomes based on vaccination status and they are willing to ask the hard questions that others dare not broach.

Dr. Aaby was one of the first scholars to study the non-specific effects of vaccines and he has become the world leader in the field. For over a century it was assumed that a vaccine only had an effect on the specific disease that was targeted. Dr. Aaby's research shows that vaccines change the immune system in ways that are unexpected. There are *positive* non-specific effects when a particular vaccine changes the immune system in ways that also provide protective effects against other diseases and *negative* non-specific effects when a vaccine changes the immune system in ways that leave one more vulnerable to other diseases.

Dr. Aaby's research in the late 1970s showed large positive effects from a measles vaccine. Children in Guinea-Bissau vaccinated against measles not only developed fewer cases of measles, they also died less frequently from other diseases as well. But in 1989, the W.H.O. introduced a new measles vaccine. Dr. Aaby and his team discovered negative non-specific effects from this formulation — girls vaccinated with the new measles vaccine died at twice the rate as unvaccinated girls.

Dr. Aaby brought his findings to the W.H.O. but it took three more years and an additional study by a team of U.S. researchers in Haiti that confirmed Dr. Aaby's original findings for the vaccine to be withdrawn.

Dr. Aaby was awarded the Novo Nordisk Prize in 2000

— the highest honor in Denmark for advances in medical science.

Over the last three decades, Dr. Aaby and his team have studied the non-specific effects of the other vaccines administered in Guinea-Bissau. His findings in connection with the DTP vaccine — the most widely administered vaccine in the world — are the most shocking. Across multiple studies, Dr. Aaby found that children vaccinated with DTP have 5 times higher (95% CI: 1.53–16.3) all-cause mortality than children who were not injected with DTP. He and his team also found sex effects — girls were more likely to die following DTP vaccination than boys.

[For those who care about science, there are also race effects from vaccines but that discussion is prohibited in the mainstream media in the U.S. because the entire vaccine program would crumble if people knew.]

Dr. Aaby describes his findings in a remarkable video HERE (transcript):

II. Christine Stabell Benn

Over the last two decades, Dr. Aaby has been joined in this research by a brilliant Danish academic named Christine Stabell Benn. In addition to researching and publishing world-class research on non-specific effects, they fell in love and married. Now Dr. Benn runs the Copenhagen office of the Bandim Health Project in addition to her other academic duties at the University of Southern Denmark. Together they've become the most formidable duo in the history of vaccine safety research and among the last honest brokers in the field.

In 2019, Dr. Benn gave a TEDx Talk at Aarhus University that summarizes their decades of research. Titled, "How vaccines train the immune system in ways no one expected" she begins by defining non-specific effects and gives examples of positive non-specific effects. But then at the 8:46 mark Benn describes their findings about the negative non-specific effects of the DTP vaccine. Click HERE.

In one slide she shows that DTP kills 5 times more kids than it saves from the three diseases it is designed to protect against. To say that publicly on camera in front of a room full of skeptical academics is one of the gutsiest things I've ever seen.

Dr. Aaby, Dr. Benn, and their team have shared their findings with the World Health Organization on multiple occasions. To date, the World Health Organization has done nothing. Indeed the W.H.O., under pressure from the Gates Foundation, uses DTP vaccination coverage rates to measure whether a country is meeting its vaccination goals (and is thus eligible for additional funding). Given that the DTP shot kills 5 times more kids than it saves, the W.H.O./Unicef vaccine program throughout the developing world is a crime against humanity that must be prosecuted by the international criminal court.

Dr. Benn goes on to explain that their massive research project has shown that three live-virus vaccines appear to offer more benefits than harms: oral polio, measles by itself (not MMR), and tuberculosis (called BCG).

But I know from my own research that these three live virus vaccines are NOT available in the U.S. (the U.S. uses an enhanced inactivated [injected] polio vaccine, MMR or MMRV, and there is a limited supply of BCG for certain high risk healthcare workers but tuberculosis is not endemic in the U.S. so it is not on the childhood schedule).

All of the other vaccines studied by BHP — adjuvanted, recombinant, and genetically engineered protein subunit vaccines — cause more harms than benefits.

So according to the best data set in the world, ALL of the vaccines on the U.S. schedule cause more harms than benefits.

Here's the part that Dr. Aaby and Dr. Benn won't tell you, but I will. The reason why these three live virus vaccines are not available in the U.S. is because all live virus vaccines eventually "revert to virulence". This means that over the years, as the virus passes through the various cell mediums that they use to grow the antigen and as the attenuated virus passes through the population, the virus evolves and changes such that eventually the vaccine will causes an outbreak of the very disease that they are trying to eliminate. That is what is happening in Africa and Pakistan right now where oral polio vaccination campaigns have triggered outbreaks of polio.

No politician wants to be responsible for an outbreak of polio, measles, or tuberculosis so they approve shelf-stable *ineffective* vaccines that cause net harms rather than the *effective* live virus vaccines that will eventually revert to virulence.

That's the dilemma and that's the starting place for any honest conversation about vaccine policy.

So when people ask, "can't I use a slowed down or spaced out schedule" I say, "the best data set in the world shows that only three vaccines produce more benefits than harms, none of those vaccines are available in the U.S., and all of the vaccines on the U.S. schedule objectively produce more harms than benefits."

You can be guided by ideology or you can be guided by the facts and those are the facts.

III. Several huge additional data points

There are a few additional facts that bear on this matter:

1. There is fairly good evidence that the 1918 Spanish

Flu Pandemic, that killed 20 to 40 million people, began
with a bacterial meningitis vaccination campaign on the
U.S. army base at Fort Riley, Kansas (and then the soldiers
recently vaccinated with a contaminated vaccine were
shipped out to fight World War I in Europe and the
pandemic went worldwide from there).

Edward Hooper, in his book The River: A Journey to
the Source of HIV and AIDS makes a compelling case that
the clinical trials for the oral polio vaccine in the Congo
may have introduced a simian retrovirus into humans that
became HIV (and contributed to the deaths of 40 million
people from AIDS).

Jeffrey Sachs, who chaired the Lancet commission on
the origins of coronavirus says that the evidence points to
SARS-CoV-2 coming from a U.S.bioweapons lab involved
in gain-of-function research. To date, 6 million people
worldwide are alleged to have died from coronavirus.

Taken together, one can make a strong case that the
three largest epidemics of the last 100 years are all
connected with the vaccine program in some way (a military vaccine campaign, a clinical trial, and gain-of-function
research).

Look, I wish none of this were true. But the mainstream
gatekeepers never fully investigate these pandemics because
they are afraid of what they might find. So it falls to independent researchers to try to piece together what happened
as best they can. If any or all of these theories are correct
then the supposed gains from vaccines over the last century
would be eclipsed by these man-made disasters.

2. Vaccine failure and harms are the business model of
the pharmaceutical industry. As Robert Kennedy Jr. points
out, prior to the introduction of mRNA shots, vaccines were
already a $50 billion a year industry that generates another

$500 billion a year in revenue for treatments for vaccine injury (including EpiPens, asthma inhalers, Risperdal, cancer treatments etc.).

As Dr. Benn explains in her TED Talk, NONE of the major pharmaceutical companies are researching live virus vaccines even though they are the only ones that work. Instead (this is me speaking again) pharmaceutical companies spend money on regulatory capture and propaganda to force dangerous and ineffective vaccines on the population because they generate at least 10 times more revenue than the effective live virus vaccines.

3. Covid-19 shots are completely ridiculous. They are objectively the most dangerous vaccines ever produced. They never should have been authorized and they cannot be made safe. They will be removed from the market. The only question is how many people they will kill before the mainstream gatekeepers admit defeat.

IV. Conclusion

The sum total of all of this is that I have become a vaccine abolitionist. Yes, I suppose one could make the case for the benefits of the three live virus vaccines. But the most powerful industry in the world blocks access to these vaccines and no politician in the U.S. will approve them lest they get blamed when the virus reverts to virulence. Given the corruption in the pharmaceutical industry, I would much rather rely on innate immunity (and natural support for my own immune system) than allow a liability-free product with untold contaminants to be injected into my body.

For all of human history, breastfeeding provided immune support to infants and playing in the dirt exposed children to microdoses of viruses and bacteria in ways that build their immune system for life. Dollar-for-dollar clean water and sanitation systems deliver much better health outcomes than vaccines.

Vaccines seemed like a good idea back in 1796. But the shots today bear little resemblance to Jenner's variolation. According to historian David Wootton, the greatest revolution in the history of medicine occurred when French hospitals in the 19th century started using statistics to record and measure health outcomes. They soon discovered that all of their interventions did not work (it led to what doctors called "therapeutic nihilism"). But the willingness to recognize those failures eventually led to scientific breakthroughs including hand-washing and antiseptics. The vaccine paradigm has objectively failed. It is time to turn the page and invest in natural support for our immune systems and *cures* (remember those?) for diseases — not monthly Pharma subscription plans for life.

I would be remiss if I didn't mention that the Biden Administration is now proposing to vastly expand the failed gene modifying public health strategy of the last two years. On Monday, Biden issued an "Executive Order on Advancing Biotechnology and Biomanufacturing Innovation for a Sustainable, Safe, and Secure American Bioeconomy" that is straight out of Brave New World. It states:

> We need to develop genetic engineering technologies and techniques to be able to *write circuitry for cells and predictably program biology in the same way in which we write software and program computers...*

The Biden administration is proposing an entire economy and society based on the bioengineering strategies of the failed mRNA vaccines. These people are literally insane.

We must commence the revolution as soon possible.

* * *

ALL VACCINES Are Unsafe & Ineffective

By Dr. Vernon Coleman, one of our great heroes. His website is vernoncoleman.org.

Things You Should Know about Traditional Vaccines. There is not a single RCT peer reviewed with true placebo control group vaccine study in existence. Not a single vaccine is necessary and safe.

You should know these things about vaccination:

1. No one else will tell you this, but some traditional vaccinations kill and maim more people than the diseases they are supposed to prevent. Historically, the evidence is clear (as I have shown in my books). American statistics also prove this. In some cases, illnesses were conquered by other means (e.g., better living conditions) before vaccines became available.

2. Essential research into vaccine safety is not done. No tests are done to see how different vaccines inter-react – or may inter-react with prescription medicines or medicines bought from the pharmacy. No one knows just how much damage is done by vaccination programmes.

3. Billions of dollars have been paid out to patients who have been injured by vaccines. And yet doctors and politicians claim that vaccines are perfectly safe.

4. Many vaccines are woefully ineffective – in addition to producing side effects. When I was a GP I never met a doctor who had the annual flu jab.

5. Every doctor I know of who has spoken out against vaccination has been struck off the medical register – usually for doubtful reasons. (I have not been struck off but I am retired.) There is nothing more likely to result in a doctor's professional ruin than speaking out against vaccination. The profession will forgive doctors who sleep with their patients, who abuse alcohol or drugs or who prescribe in a dangerous way. But those who question vaccination (particularly childhood vaccination programmes) are never forgiven.

6. The media (including the internet) has been instructed not to allow any debate or discussion of vaccination side effects, dangers or shortcomings. No one will debate vaccination with me anymore. The BBC refuses to allow any discussion of vaccination and will not allow anyone questioning vaccination onto its programmes 'whether they are right or wrong'. On the internet, articles questioning the effectiveness or safety of vaccination are suppressed. I'm a Sunday Times bestselling author with over two million books sold in the UK and books translated into 25 languages. But when over 600 copies of my book on vaccination (*Anyone who tells you vaccines are safe and effective is lying*) were sent out to newspapers and magazines, not one review was

ever published. Some publications were so terrified by the book that instead of selling it (as is customary with review copies) they sent it back to me.

7. I have been threatened, lied about and fired because of my campaigning. My phones are tapped. My website has been hacked into on many occasions (one website alone is hacked over 3,000 times a month) and destroyed twice. I've been threatened with lawsuits more times than I can remember. I've had private detectives nosing into my life and process servers banging on my door. One writ server from drug companies brought so much paperwork he had to put it through the cat flap – it wouldn't go through the letter box. And there was one threatened ` hit' which Interpol thought serious enough to merit investigation. There is an old Japanese saying: "The nail that sticks out gets pounded down" which seems appropriate.

Vernon Coleman's book, Anyone Who Tells You Vaccines are Safe and Effective is Lying is available as a paperback and an eBook.

* * *

STEVE KIRSCH agrees.

He quotes an Amazon review of Gabriela Probst's book exposing vaccines, *Turtles All the Way Down*:

Cassandra's Memo

5.0 out of 5 stars Stunning evaluation of the vaccine industry

Reviewed in the United States on September 5, 2022

An absolutely devastating takedown of the vaccine industry, especially coming on the heels of the 'safe and effective' Covid shots, which are actually neither. This book was published in 2019 but was just recently translated into English. None of the facts stated have been refuted by anyone in the vaccine industry.

Did you know there has never been one completely randomized control trial done with ANY of the vaccines on the market to test for safety? Not one. So efficacy aside, there is literally NO science to back up the claim that any vaccine is safe for infants, small children, or adults.

Did you know that only a small handful of the current 'required' vaccines confer any kind of herd immunity? About 70% of them possibly provide some personal protection for the recipient, but most of the target diseases are mild anyway and easily survivable, thus completely negating any kind of societal need for mass vaccination.

Did you know that the Salk and Sabin polio shots had a negligible effect on the reduction of polio cases, and in fact, there's a vast amount of evidence that points to pesticide poisoning as the cause of the paralysis heretofore attributed to polio?

Did you know that chronic conditions in children have EXPLODED in the last 60 years or so, since vaccines have been pushed on an unsuspecting public, with no honest attempt to explain or stop the explosion? Every doctor/researcher who has even tried to examine this has been discredited, blackballed, and had their studies suppressed. Government and Big Pharma fund virtually ALL scientific research and they have zero incentive to find anything negative in the vaccine program.

Run, don't walk, from anyone trying to inject your defenseless baby with any of the vaccines. The risk/benefit analysis comes down squarely on the side of not vaxxing.

Do your research; do NOT listen to the pediatrician who has no training in this field. Ask the questions that are suggested in this book and see what kind of response you get.

I am convinced that my youngest child, 16 years his eldest sibling's junior, and recipient of almost 2X as many shots in infancy and early childhood, has a chronic skin condition and some minor developmental delays as a result of the aluminum, mercury, thimerosal, and other toxic poisons in the myriad shots I was ignorant enough to allow him to receive. I thank God for the fact that this is ALL he's suffering from and that he's not irredeemably harmed.

It's too late for a lot of kids, but maybe this book can educate the next generation of parents, and they can save their kids from a lifetime of illness and vaccine induced misery.

Chapter 23
Dissolving My Vaxxed Illusions by Unbekoming

Waking up to vaccination malfeasance has really gotten to me, and I've been wondering why it would bug me so much.

— Unbekoming on Substack

S ubscribe to him HERE, his archive is HERE, and HERE is the link for *Vaxxed* 2, the must-listen video about vaccines from the Children's Health Defense website.

* * *

I arrived in Australia in late 1992, having left war-torn Iraq. I chose to leave an authoritarian state and start a new life in what I considered to be the best address on earth. It never crossed my mind that the free state I ran towards was built on an invisible yet highly sophisticated authoritarian government-corporate fascist enterprise. It bullied its population to inject its children with multiple dangerous disease-causing chemicals... for the greater good.

SUBSTACK LINK

* * *

Multigenerational indoctrination is real. Prisons of the mind are real.

And so it is that the two beautiful children we brought into this "free land," we injected with those chemicals, giving them a range of conditions that included:

- Stutter and delayed speech development
- Hyperactivity
- Asthma
- Vitiligo
- Hay fever

A fascist totalitarian enterprise managed to sleepwalk me into doing this.

I wonder, are you hypnotized, or are you free?

I gradually come to terms with all this. To help you understand, I am going to meander around this vaccination rabbit hole for quite some time.

Cassandra's Memo

I'm about two-thirds through *Dissolving Illusions*, and without a doubt, it's one of the most important books I have ever read. Books that reorient you to reality are pretty rare, and this is one of them.

The book has 2100 five-star Amazon reviews. It also has a website that includes a gallery of photos and graphs to help you see the decline and virtual vanishing of disease BEFORE vaccinations came along.

Graphs & Images - *Dissolving Illusions | Disease, Vaccines, and the Forgotten History*

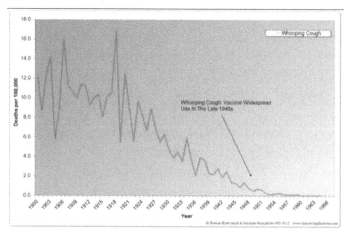

Whooping cough (pertussis) in the US.

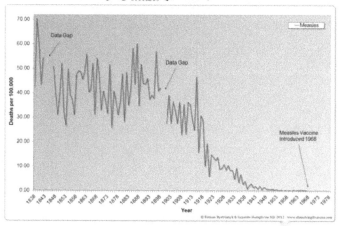

Measles in England/Wales.

The two graphs above prove that both measles and whooping cough were nearly extinct when their respective vaccines were introduced.

The most important part of this post and the easiest way to understand the subject is *Vaxxed 2*, a stunning, profoundly important 2016 documentary. It will convince you that vaccinations cause autism and more. It is heavily censored, but you can view it by clicking the first link in this post.

If you have little kids that you are injecting according to "the schedule," especially if you have a baby on the way, this is required viewing. You will see firsthand what vaccine injury looks like, but even more importantly, you will see in the last 30 minutes what unvaccinated children look like. As tearful as I was listening to the injured, seeing what real health looks like in children who have never had a single injection is something else again. Family after family comes on screen and tells you that they have NEVER needed to take their child to a doctor, that they NEVER had an ear infection, and that they NEVER had to take an antibiotic. Human natural immunity, when left undamaged, turns out to be a powerful shield against disease.

Watching these super healthy children come on camera one after another made me think back to Robert Kennedy, Jr., in his Tyson interview where he said:

> All [of these injuries] are directly linked to vaccines in the scientific literature. On our website we have 1,400 peer reviewed studies published on NIH's website PubMed, linking various vaccines to all of those injuries.
>
> Well, they're making $60 billion a year selling us vaccines, but they're making $500 billion a year selling the remedies for the injuries caused by vaccines.

The two least profitable versions of humanity are dead people and healthy people.

The most profitable version is an unhealthy person. They have the greatest "lifetime value," as an MBA would say if they were studying profits. The system leans towards "unhealth" and sustaining itself. Unhealth sustains. Health doesn't.

Witnessing the better health of the unvaccinated, I couldn't help but reflect on the conditions we gave our kids. Mine got off lightly, as you will see from the stories of the injured.

The documentary exposes Gardasil (HPV vaccine), and Gardasil-injured kids. Again, this was something that we sleepwalked our daughter into.

The theory is that it will help prevent cervical cancer in girls and penile cancer in boys, but both claims are lies. At 42 minutes Robert Kennedy, Jr., explains that children who take the vaccine are 37x more likely to die from the vaccine than from cervical cancer.

Watch this documentary and get others to watch it. It might be the only place where you will see what healthy unvaccinated kids and people look like.

Dissolving Illusions' foreword by Dr. Jayne L. M. Donegan is wonderful:

> Vaccination is regarded as the most important health advance in the 20th century by most health professionals and laypeople. Although the dramatic decreases in morbidity and mortality from diseases that occurred in the course of the 20th century have been credited to the introduction of specific vaccines, scant acknowledgment has been given to improving social conditions.
>
> Despite questioning the safety and efficacy of vaccination by reputable medical men since its introduction, debate has been, and is, increasingly discouraged.
>
> Information published in scientific journals is used to support this position, other views being regarded as "unscientific."

Cassandra's Memo

It was a received "article of faith" for me and my contemporaries that vaccination was the single most useful health intervention that had ever been introduced. Along with all my medical and nursing colleagues, I was taught that vaccines were the reason children and adults stopped dying from diseases for which there are vaccines.

We were told that other diseases, such as scarlet fever, rheumatic fever, typhus, typhoid, cholera, and so on, for which there were no vaccines at the time, diminished both in incidence and mortality (ability to kill) due to better social conditions.

This is such an obvious point!

If vaccines got rid of a disease, did they get rid of every single disease? If not, what happened to the diseases that vaccines didn't "save us from?" They just seemed to go away... why? Yep, you guessed it: water, nutrition, sanitation, sewerage, and improved working conditions. Back to Donegan:

> You would think—as medical students who are supposed to be moderately intelligent—that some of us would have asked, "But if deaths from these diseases decreased due to improved social conditions, mightn't the ones for which there are vaccines also have decreased at the same time, for the same reason?" But we didn't.
>
> The medical curriculum is so overloaded with information that you just have to learn what you hear, as you hear it: nonvaccinatable diseases into the social conditions box and vaccinatable diseases into the vaccines box and then on to the next subject.
>
> Everything I was taught and read in textbooks, both

before I qualified as a doctor and through all my post-graduate training, reinforced this view.

Along with most doctors, I regarded parents who would not vaccinate their children as ignorant or, if not ignorant, sociopathic. They were withholding what I believed was a lifesaving intervention and putting every-body else at risk by reducing herd immunity.

Many brave doctors show up for interviews in *Vaxxed 2*. They are all asked what they were taught at university about vaccines, and they all say the same thing. Pretty much nothing, just that there is a childhood vaccine schedule and that the kids need to stick to it. They even manage to get an immunologist (with a Ph.D.) onto the show... the same thing.

Nothing on risks, all on benefit... just make sure the kids get it.

These are the foot soldiers of a drug cartel, and I do not give them a pass. They might not get taught properly at university, but when they are let loose on the public, they shut down their curiosity. And pediatricians are the abso-lute worst.

In Forrest Maready's short book *Unvaccinated*, towards the end, he talks about what medical students study at university about vaccination.

Physicians may spend a few hours learning the schedules recommended by the government and spend a few hours learning which vaccines should be administered subcuta-neously (under the skin) as opposed to intra-muscularly. Beyond that, they learn almost nothing about vaccines.

I was so confused by hearing this; I bought every book listed on the medical curriculum of a prestigious medical school. I even bought some auxiliary books that were not required but on the optional, "recommended" reading list. After going through each and every book on the list—thousands and thousands of pages—there were only four pages that talked about how vaccines work! There were 11 pages that listed the vaccine schedule recommended by the government, but besides that, 4 pages that talked about vaccines.

I made a video about it, showing the books and how little a prestigious medical school's curriculum spent teaching about vaccines. Many doctors and nurses got in touch with me to confirm this had been their experience in medical school. Of course, students learn more than what is taught from their schoolbooks, but I imagine the disparity continues into their classroom and residencies.

Once I understood that doctors and nurses learn very little about vaccines in school, I began to realize why they are so hostile to people like myself who ask honest questions about them. I have written books on the subject, but there are many, many amateur anti-vaxxer mothers and fathers out there who are much, much smarter than me. Any of us could easily stump an average pediatric doctor or nurse on vaccines with some of our common knowledge.

Now, back to *Dissolving Illusions* and Dr. Jayne L. M. Donegan:

Indeed, at special clinics in the 1980s, I used to counsel parents who wouldn't vaccinate their children against whooping cough, which was regarded as the problematic vaccine in those days. I acknowledged that there were dangers associated with the vaccine. I was a truthful doctor, but I told them the official line that the disease was 10 times more likely to cause death or disability than the vaccine, so any sane person would choose to vaccinate.

What changed?

In 1994 there was a massive measles/rubella vaccination campaign in the UK. Seven million schoolchildren were vaccinated against measles and rubella to protect them from an epidemic of measles, which was said to be imminent.

In those days, there was only one measles shot in the schedule—it is a live viral vaccine and was supposed to be like the wild measles virus. We were told, "One dose and you are immune for life." I did realize that one shot, however, might not protect every child—no vaccine is one hundred per cent effective—but the chief medical officer said that even two shots of this "one-shot vaccine" would not necessarily protect children when the epidemic came and that they would need a third. He also said that the best way to vaccinate children was en masse to "break the chain of transmission."

This left me in a quandary. Obviously, the risk-to-benefit ratio of the vaccine was in favor of the vaccine if it was safer than the disease and if it stopped your child from getting the disease. This is what most parents expect to happen and certainly what they are encouraged to believe.

But if children can have the one-shot vaccine twice and still get the disease, so they need to have a third shot, this means they can be exposed to all the risks of the vaccine two or three times... and at the same time, all the risks of the disease as well. Did I need to reevaluate what I had been saying to parents?

Also, if the best way of "breaking the chain of transmission" of an infectious disease was to vaccinate en masse, why did we vaccinate babies with all those different vaccines at two, three, and four months of age (UK schedule)? Why didn't we just wait for two or three years and then vaccinate all those who had been born in the interim en masse to break the chain of transmission?

Good questions! She goes on:

This was the start of my long, slow journey researching vaccination and disease ecology and learning about other models and philosophies of health and natural hygiene such as those used by the great pioneers who cleaned up our cities and built clean water supplies and sewage systems. I spent hours in libraries looking at archived journals and textbooks and the Office for National Statistics (ONS) getting out dusty volumes from the middle of the 19th century to make graphs of death rates from diseases for which we have vaccines but which, for some reason, have not been drawn - or made available to doctors or parents by the ONS or the Department of Health.

I read what prominent men of science, medical officers for health, and doctors wrote about vaccination and its sequelae that never made it into today's textbooks and found out what anyone with even a passing acquaintance with disease figures of the 19th and 20th century knew. For example, by the 1950s when the whooping cough vaccine was introduced, data showed that whooping cough was killing only 1 percent of the numbers of people who used to die in England and Wales 50 years before.

Official data showed that the same happened with measles. Indeed, when the measles vaccine was introduced to the UK in 1968, the death rate continued to drop steadily, even though the initial uptake of the vaccine was only 30 percent and didn't get above 50 percent until the 1980s.

Even the much-heralded success story of smallpox vaccination was not what it seemed. The enforcement of the compulsory smallpox vaccination law in 1867, when the death rate was already falling, was accompanied by an increase in the deaths from 100 to 400 deaths per million.

Yes, the "holy" smallpox vaccine managed to increase smallpox death and prolong widespread smallpox disease for about a century. Smallpox vaccination is one of the greatest man-made medical disasters, exactly the opposite of what all medical textbooks and Google will tell you.

As I recently described HERE, the Covid vaccination is another calamity. It too was manufactured by doctors, governments, and corporations. As Dr. Jayne L. M. Donegan wrote, "After overcoming an awful lot of fear, I came to the gradual realization that it was true what people on the outside had been telling me—that 'health is the only immunity.' We don't need protecting from 'out there.'"

Chapter 24
Bill Gates Slaughtered Fetuses Using Tetanus Vaccine Spiked With Pregnancy Hormone

When they're through with Africa, they're coming
for you.

> — Dr. Steven Karanja, an obstetrician
> whistleblower against the Gates'
> depopulation plot in Kenya

Karanja predicted the conspiracy's worldwide attack on us. He died in April 2021, and his death was officially attributed to Covid. Leadership is the lynchpin of history. Without Churchill, Lincoln, Washington, or Eisenhower, we would be living in a different world. We also have monsters— Stalin, Hitler, and Mao. Genghis Kahn and his armies slit the throats and raped the women of those they conquered. His genes survive in 16 million men today.

Gates is today's mafia don of genocide. He pushed Depo-Provera in Africa, a birth control shot that damages women's health and occasionally kills them. This was long before he trafficked the Covid jab.

193

Do you trust him? Photo credit: Hands-on: Bill Gates
holding a vaccine for meningitis, 2011. Anja
Niedringhaus/AP photo.

SUBSTACK LINK

Diabolical Agenda is a short movie about this tragedy
on the Children's Heath Defense website HERE. "More
Harm Than Good," Chapter 10 of *The Real Anthony
Fauci,* tells more (see the movie HERE). Here is an excerpt:

> Gates's fetish for reducing population is a family pedi-
> gree. His father, Bill Gates Sr., was a prominent corpo-
> rate lawyer and civic leader in Seattle with a lifelong
> obsession for "population control." Gates Sr. sat on the
> national board of Planned Parenthood, a neo-progressive
> organization founded in 1916 by the racist eugenicist

Margaret Sanger to promote birth control and sterilization and to purge "human waste" and "create a race of
thoroughbreds."59 Sanger said she hoped to purify the
gene pool by "eliminating the unfit" persons with disabilities—preventing such persons from reproducing60 by
surgical sterilization or other means...

Gates has made a long parade of public statements
and investments that reflect his deep dread of overpopulation. He describes himself as an admirer and proponent of the population doomsayer Paul Ehrlich, author of
The Population Bomb, whom Gates describes as "the
world's most prominent environmental Cassandra,"
meaning a prophet who accurately predicts misfortune
or disaster...

[One] of Gates's earliest philanthropic undertakings
was a 2002 project to administer tetanus vaccines to
poor women in fifty-seven countries. ...critics credibly
suggest that these vaccines may have been secretly laced
with a formula the Rockefeller Foundation developed to
sterilize women against their will.

Chapter 25
Diversion: Trying to Save My Beloved Children From the Vax

Dearest ones:

You know who I mean—you three with the high salaries and IQs. Parents should beam unconditional positive regard to their kids, but we are past that. I would continue to endure your naïve actions in silence, but you are making mistakes from which you may never recover. You have not read the memo despite having it sent to you many times. Your intellectual arrogance is a suit of clothes that looks terrible on anyone, so listen to me for once and earn my respect.

One of you recently accused me behind my back of being a Republican, but I assure you that I am innocent of that. I am simply pro-life—your life. At 68, what do I have left besides you? I may not live to see the destruction of your health and freedoms, but you will if you do not wake up. Strain yourself to see through the dark glass--it is time to give up childish things, speak like adults, and act like adults.

Review the following basics. There is no controversy about any of it.

Our country's foundation is freedom of speech. This is

a principle rather than a narrowly interpreted law. Since censorship became more aggressive in 2020, we have been easily fooled. The mainstream media, the social media, and the scientific literature are sewers, and their filth has made distinguishing right from wrong difficult. Only a few platforms, such as substack.com, continue free of interference. I hope they last.

Covid was financed by US sources, made in a lab, and used as a weapon. We have decades of proof, including patents, testimony, viral genetics, and financial records.

Simple and effective treatments for similar viral diseases have existed for a decade and were proven effective against Covid in early 2020. These include vitamin D, zinc, ivermectin, hydroxychloroquine, steroids, and, recently, monoclonal antibodies. Concealing these or making them unavailable using lies and propaganda resulted in millions of unnecessary deaths.

Over 1000 studies have proven that the "vaccines" are toxic, sometimes fatal, and much worse than doing nothing. To continue the lies, the WHO changed the definition of vaccine. Since the shot was introduced, robust death data from insurance companies and the US military has shown about a 40 percent increase in overall population-wide fatalities. It has killed—at least—hundreds of thousands of people in the US alone.

We cannot predict the longer-term effects of the vax because our experience is brief. But we know that the spike proteins in the jab concentrate in the female reproductive organs. It kills over half the fetuses if given to pregnant mothers. The evidence that they also produce infertility is conclusive (see The Covid and Vax disaster Part 3). Some have developed AIDS-like syndromes, but it is too early to determine how many will be affected. We know that every injection increases the chances of injury and death.

Who is responsible? Clear, open, and convincing documentary evidence convicts the world bankers, the World Economic Forum (WEF), and many billionaires. China and the rogue Pharma companies are also accessories to the genocide. Some of these groups are financial opportunists, but the primary players want totalitarian control.

Events in Australia foreshadow their next moves. Here, Chinese-style social credit scores are being implemented. In a similar move, Trudeau, a WEF puppet, froze the assets of those who donated to the truckers. Vax cards with QR codes are now being offered in more than 30 US states. If implemented, the government's ability to inject us with whatever they want on the threat of financial penalties could become a brutal reality.

Our governments have been destroying our currencies through money printing. These are the worst financial crimes in history, and the coming hyperinflation is an economic Tower of Babel that will impoverish us. Implementing digital currencies could complete their control (Bitcoin alone is decentralized, outside their command, and will hopefully remain an alternative).

We have recently been saved from Covid by the development of omicron. It creates immunity and poses little risk. But do not expect it to protect us from the global predators trying to eat our lunch along with theirs. You are now hearing messages about the horrors of hemorrhagic fever, "VAIDS," and exotic Covid strains with new Latin letters. Do your best to ignore it all and focus on yourself. For example, get your assets sheltered. The traditional advice is gold, real estate, and possibly Bitcoin, but I make no recommendations. Predicting the future is a fool's game.

Cassandra's Memo

So awake, arise, look around, and take your intellect in hand. Get out of the internet box. Ignore wiki, google, and social media sources. Turn away with disdain when you hear "conspiracy theory," "debunked," "quackery," "antivaccine," "hesitancy," or "misinformation." Realize that "fact-checking" is faked and controlled. Understand that people like me are now called "domestic terrorists." Fire yourself from your job if necessary to avoid mandates. Consider relocating. I am writing from Florida, and you might also consider Texas, Tennessee, and Idaho.

I love you, and I hope we are all still here in two years. —Robert

Unbekoming wrote a similar letter to his family HERE.

Part Six

At Least Half of Prescription Drugs Do More Harm Than Good

Chapter 26
Tim Alexander is an Expert on Medication Toxicity

The reason doctors are so dangerous is that they believe in what they are doing.

— Robert S. Mendelsohn, MD

T im Alexander works with tens of thousands of people whose lives have been ruined by prescription drugs. Here are the events that threw him into the arena.

SUBSTACK LINK for Tim's interview.

Tim (left) and Pastor Cedric Anderson (right) during
the wedding ceremony.

Cedric Anderson, a pastor and Tim's friend, conducted
Tim's marriage to his wife, Karen.

Soon after, Pastor Anderson married Tim's cousin,
Karen Smith (a second Karen). But Anderson became
erratic, paranoid, and delusional. Karen S. moved out after
six weeks. A short time later, the pastor went to the school
where Karen Smith taught. He shot and killed his new wife,
a bystander, and then himself. It was a nationwide media
outcry for two months, and he was dubbed the San
Bernadino shooter.

Anderson's family found a grab-bag of psych drugs
among his possessions. No one knew he was taking SSRI
(Prozac class) antidepressants, not even his mother. These
are proven causes of violence and suicide. But no mention
of Anderson's medications made it into the media because
big Pharma pays for nearly all TV news and 75 percent of
TV advertising.

Mr. Alexander kept asking himself how such an impossible event could have happened to people he knew and
loved. Since documentary filmmakers like Tim are detectives, he formed a Facebook group called "Legal Death—In
Drugs We Trust" that sought to uncover drug side effects.

Within a few months, it grew to 30,000 people and 3500 daily posts. He read all the stories. Many were about suicide and violent behavior.

Tim asked the people in his group with the worst prescription drug catastrophes to speak to him in person. He and Karen went on the two-month, 16,500-mile road trip to film them.

Tim and Karen's route.

Their stories were horrific. Many of the people he spoke to were bed-bound and neurologically damaged.

Tim learned that many medications considered harmless could cause severe damage. For example, he learned about the toxicity of Cipro and gadolinium contrast dye. He saw cases where they were used together with devastating results. Tim directed a full-length feature film about the drug disasters he saw on his trip.

Although Mr. Alexander is not a physician, he has compiled an archive of drug information through his interviews and years doing Facebook moderation. This work has made him a top authority on prescription medication side effects and damages. What makes Tim different from other experts is that he explored many drug classes rather than specializing in a few.

Tim has had difficulty getting his film distributed. Since Pharma controls the media, to free it for general viewing, he needs to raise about $200,000 to pay his investors back. Contact him if you want to help, and he will show you the movie. I have seen it, and its quality is superb. His email is timacs@me.com.

Chapter 27
Dermatologists Butcher Patients With Accutane

Patients are misinformed about the risks and harmed everywhere in the world where isotretinoin (Accutane) is prescribed.

— Rochelle

S he sent me the following email about her experiences, and I interviewed her.

* * *

Hello, Dr. Yoho,

I read your book last year and valued your insights. Tim Alexander interviewed me for his documentary, Legal Death in Drugs We Trust, *and I recently listened to your interview with him.*

I am Rochelle Nisam, a magna cum laude graduate in premedical biological sciences from UC Santa Cruz with advanced biosciences post-baccalaureate studies in pharmacology, toxicology, physiology, microbiology, and human genetics from UC Berkeley. Like you, I was a rock climbing enthusiast, but unfortunately, I can't climb now because I'm permanently disabled. I was "born into medicine" - my entire family is nurses or doctors. My grandfather was the physician for the King of Afghanistan and the Afghan Olympic team. I was taught from a young age to trust doctors because my father, Dr. Merrill Nisam, is a pulmonologist, ICU director, and associate professor of internal medicine at UCSF.

I excelled in school and was accepted for competitive research positions, TAships and internships. I was supposed to be a veterinarian or medical doctor by now. Despite my potential, I have been physically disabled and mostly house-bound/bedbound for the past eight years, living a nightmare of severe chronic pain and illness with a wide array of incurable symptoms. I've tried many treatments with no signs of improvement. My prognosis is dismal.

I was first injured by Gardasil (HPV vaccine) at age 20 and subsequently by drugs used to treat the various issues I developed. I had severe cystic acne, brain fog, mood swings, cognitive issues, dissociative periods, memory problems, severe depression, anxiety, etc. I was gaslit by doctors and prescribed several psychiatric medicines for the neuropsychi-

*atric effects of the HPV vaccine. I had reactions to
isotretinoin that I was prescribed for cystic acne.*

Note: Accutane is the original brand name for this drug,
but the manufacturer was repeatedly sued and took it off
the market in 2009. Patients were becoming psychotic,
committing suicide, and having many other horrendous side
effects, including "rhabdomyolysis" or muscle degeneration.
Some courts have absolved generic manufacturers of
liability for drug harms, claiming that the original manufacturer did the studies and was the sole responsible party. See
the "Prozac and relatives" chapter of Butchered by "Healthcare" for more. Only generic Accutane remains on the US
market.

*I was concerned about taking isotretinoin because of the
lawsuits, but my dermatologist (who shared an office with my
father) reassured me that all lawsuits had been dropped and
isotretinoin had recently been "scientifically proven" to cause
no ill effects. He promised me it was safe at a "low dose" and
that he had prescribed it thousands of times with no problems. While taking the medication, I felt mostly fine. My
dose was low, my monthly bloodwork was all normal, and I
had no headaches, digestive problems, or signs of organ toxicity, so I did not foresee any issues. However, I have since
discovered that this medicine has a latent toxic potential. It
may cause widespread stem cell death, DNA damage, and
mitochondrial damage. The resulting symptoms and adverse
health effects may occur months or even years after discontinuation.*

*That's exactly what happened. The real nightmare
started months after my last pill. After three months, I developed intermittent tremors and collapsed in a yoga class. Four
months later, I developed random migrating pains and
periods of weakness while rock climbing. Six months after*

my last pill, I woke up suddenly one day unable to walk. I felt like I was hit by a bus and had the onset of the crippling problems that I still have today. These were neurological (memory problems, myalgic encephalomyelitis / CFS, migraines, cognitive issues, brain fog, low blood pressure, POTS, neuropathy, dizziness, weakness, visual snow) and musculoskeletal (severe tendon, ligament, joint, bone, and muscle damage). Before this, I could do two-finger pull-ups, V5 boulder problems, 5.11d top-ropes, and 5.10 sport climbs. But within 24 hours, I was almost entirely bedbound and unable to walk or use my hands. I experienced partial paralysis in my hands and could not move my fingers or grasp anything for several weeks. My neuropsychiatric and cognitive abilities dramatically changed—according to a neurologist, my memory had declined from significantly above average to now in the lowest 20th percentile.

No doctor I saw believed this was possible. It was not a risk that dermatologists seem to know about. For years, I was gaslit by medical professionals and even my own family. I was homeless for periods because my family didn't believe my illness or symptoms were real. However, I found many thousands - perhaps millions - of young people like me who developed severe health problems months or even years after stopping isotretinoin.

Dermatology organizations lie about the risks of this medication, and pharmaceutical companies fund fraudulent research disputing the dangers and adverse effects. Dermatologists tell patients that side effects are "reversible" and that it is impossible to develop effects once the medicine is no longer in your body. This is not true. There are no FDA warnings about many of the permanent neurological side effects I experienced or that side effects may start months or years after the drug's discontinuation. This is just like fluoro-

quinolone antibiotics, which carry a warning about latent effects.

In 2019, I checked social media to see what dermatologists were saying about this. Have they since added new warnings or changed the way they inform patients? I was shocked at what I discovered—the American Academy of Dermatology has been organizing aggressive campaigns instructing dermatologists to use social media to "fight the online rumors" and "misinformation" about isotretinoin. And PubMed articles on how to combat the "false information" about isotretinoin have popped up in recent years. Articles about isotretinoin "misinformation" on TikTok, social media, and Facebook have been published, describing people spreading "false rumors" about the side effects. I found MANY dermatologists with prestigious medical degrees using YouTube, TikTok, Facebook, and Instagram, which directly target children and youth—to promote and advertise isotretinoin. They falsely claim that the rumors about certain serious adverse events and long-term effects are "myths".

These dermatologists and dermatological associations are using social media as an advertisement vehicle to push this harmful chemotherapy drug on children with a minor, often temporary skin issue. And I discovered that the roots of this corruption were far deeper: pharmaceutical companies, including Roche, Sun Pharma, and Dr. Reddy's laboratories, funded research that was used as marketing. The studies were poorly conducted and likely fraudulent. They concluded that isotretinoin does NOT cause the inflammatory bowel disease OR neuropsychiatric disorders (depression, suicidality). Since then, the AAD guidelines for isotretinoin prescribing have recently changed to recommend this treatment as a first-line therapy instead of the last resort for all types of cystic acne.

Additionally, they recommend it for mild to moderate acne. And so prescriptions have skyrocketed— today, most users who are prescribed this toxic pill do NOT have severe or even deeply cystic acne. Most of them are teenagers.

Some dermatologists have even gone on record admitting to prescribing these pills "like candy" to children "as young as seven years old." There are even case reports in the medical literature recommending isotretinoin for infantile acne! The situation is entirely out of control. Every year, more kids and young adults in online support groups end their lives due to severe and irreversible health problems. Many are chronically ill and permanently bedbound like me. Dermatologists with millions of followers on social media continue to laugh at the idea that their favorite pill could harm anyone, claiming it is "extremely safe", as long as patients don't get pregnant and take monthly labs. One Instagram-famous dermatologist told me to "go take Accutane and die" when I debated his online drug promotion. Despite showing his false claims and advice to "go die" to the state medical board, this dermatologist still has his medical license—and nearly 100,000 followers on Instagram.

I have collected extensive data and written a literature review on this topic. I have hundreds of files of screenshots, videos, and social media comments of board-certified dermatologists promoting isotretinoin on social media. They make false claims about the low risks and claim that the long-term damage I have had personally and seen in other patients is just an "online rumor"/"myth" and not real. Furthermore, I learned through openpaymentsdata.cms.gov that the AAD leaders, board members, and journal editors received $76 million from pharmaceutical companies between 2014 to 2020.

Upon discovering these extensive corruption and misin-

formation campaigns, I decided to organize advocacy efforts to expose these dangerous lies. First, I contacted numerous medical organizations, including the AMA medical ethics committee, the FDA, the AAD, and the ABD, dozens of times. Using dozens of pages of indisputable evidence, I complained about the dermatologists' false claims and promotion of generic Accutane on social media. For several months, I sent dozens of emails to over 60 physician board members and leaders of these organizations. My father, Dr. Merrill Nisam, also sent emails pleading for this issue to be examined.

When we were both stonewalled, I organized multiple survivors and family members of isotretinoin victims to send emails to these medical organizations. We begged them to address the issue. When that didn't work, I created a petition against the dermatologists making false claims and collected hundreds of signatures to send to medical organizations. Continuously ignored, we began using social media in a peaceful protest attempt to publicly call attention to the "social media celebrity" dermatologists' lies. We included scientific evidence to explain the situation. I never received any responses. I was, however, told that the president of the AAD "knows all about me". He sent an email to all AAD members nationwide, warning them about "Accutane trolls" who are "critical of perceived side effects", and suggesting they ignore our efforts. He also instructed the member to contact law enforcement if anyone contacted them about the issue or criticized their medical claims.

Shortly after these advocacy attempts, the AAD issued a new position statement designed to fight the "myths" about the drug. It stated that the side effects are "temporary." This statement has since been removed, but I have evidence in screenshots. My family started receiving threatening phone calls, and my father was harassed at work and threatened with litigation for signing a petition against the false claims made by the AAD and dermatologists. My personal information was doxxed, and someone called my parents' home at 3 AM and asked for me in an intimidating voice. I contacted Dr. Doug Bremner, who wrote a book called The Goose Who Laid the Golden Egg, about his experience with corporate intimidation and home invasions following his research on isotretinoin's adverse effects on the brain. He was not surprised to hear about the harassment. Several other advocates have also reported receiving disturbing threats that forced some of them into silence.

Several Facebook groups have thousands of members who Accutane and its generics harmed. I've also spoken to hundreds of patients damaged by isotretinoin. None of them were fully warned about the long-term risks. All of them were told that side effects are "reversible upon discontinuation," and that new or worsening effects after discontinuation of the drug is "impossible." I have spoken to young victims of this scandal from America, the UK, Australia, New Zealand, Ireland, France, Hungary, Russia, Ukraine, Germany, Poland, Brazil, Chile, Mexico, India, Saudi Arabia, Italy, Pakistan, China, and even Afghanistan.

Sincerely,
Rochelle Nisam

SUBSTACK LINK for Rochelle's interview

Dermatologists promoting Accutane:

1. Dr. Mudgil stating side effects are transient (short clip, 40 seconds)
2. Dr. Mudgil: "6 months of pain for a lifetime of gain" (short clip, 15 seconds)
3. Dr. Spierings denies long-term effects (1 min)
4. Dr. Spierings claims she would never give a systemically harmful medication for acne (1 min).
5. Pediatric dermatologist Dr. Carla Torres-Zegarra "I find myself sometimes giving Accutane like candy" (short clip)
6. Dr. Natalia Spierings: "I've given it to 7-year-olds" (short clip)
7. Long list of effects Dr. Spierings denies (3 min)
8. Conversation between Dr. Torres and Dr. Spierings denying long-term effects (6-min conversation).
9. Dr. Dray stating back and joint pain is "temporary."

10. Dr. Angelo Landriscina: "Just take the damn Accutane already, there is no reason to be afraid" (short clip).
11. Dr. Marius Rademaker treating 6-month infant with Accutane for acne (short clip).
12. Dr. Julie Harper: "It's hard to get too young for isotretinoin."
13. Dr. Elizabeth Swanson: No "rules or regulations" about how young you can go (prescribed to 9-year-old).
14. Dr. Julie Harper & Dr. Jonette Keri: "get that isotretinoin going sooner" (for mild acne).
15. Celebrity Dermatologist Dr. Mudgil publicly lies to followers about Accutane long-term effects

RxExposed is another YouTube channel about drug abuse.

HERE is a link to Rochelle's entire channel; to find the playlist, click on the "playlist" heading and look at the individual video clips.

* * *

RELATED: the start of The Dermatology Charade chapter in *Butchered by "Healthcare:"*

I tried to become a dermatologist once. These specialists stay cleverly in their own world, avoid dealing with serious problems, and make a lot of money without losing sleep. It seemed like a masterful concept. I was an annoying young man, but through family connections and somehow conjuring a fragile veneer of charm, I got accepted into one of their most selective training programs. I thought this feat qualified me for the dermatologic lifestyle and wanted to spend my weekends hiking the Appalachian Trail. My mentors, however, thought I should spend 70 hours a week learning skin disease. After a year, they exposed me as a poseur and kicked me out.

I viewed it as a personal failure, but I smelled something fishy the whole time. I was too close to see clearly and had plenty of problems, so I could not put my finger on it. Like the dermatologists who were unsuccessfully trying to train me, I did not know the history.

The modern era for skin doctors started in the 1980s when the American Academy of Dermatology hatched a plan to contrive an epidemic of dangerous skin cancers. A Madison Avenue public relations firm charged them two million dollars to develop the idea. The proposal was for them to disease-monger themselves from foolish pimple poppers into fierce cancer fighters. After this, they evangelized about patients coming to their offices for a complete skin examination. This would supposedly prevent a plague of skin cancers. The USPSTF later exposed this idea as worthless and said the screening frenzy was cultivating lucrative skin surgery rather than preventing cancer.

Chapter 28
Diversion: Other Risks Beside Drugs

Almost everything scares me these days.

— Dick Cilley, hobo climber, said this while
risking his life

D angers are universal and unavoidable. Here are examples from law, surgery, and climbing. I nearly killed myself at the cliff pictured above.

* * *

Choosing a lawyer is hazardous. I had drinks with a sixty-year-old attorney who said he had never made a mistake with a client. I tried to be polite for a few minutes and asked him to tell me more. He said he had worked for thirty-five years, never had a bad result, or missed a deadline. I listened for a while, wondering—did he believe what he was saying? I realized I was sitting with a narcissist who had little self-awareness or, more likely, a sociopath testing me for gullibility. I walked out in the middle of a sentence and never looked back.

SUBSTACK LINK

* * *

Physicians must take risks, and surgeons are continually reminded of their errors, sometimes by the lawyers who specialize in suing us. We make hundreds of decisions daily and understand mistakes. Although most are neither consequential nor result in damage, all of us have seen patients injured, and many of us worry constantly. For example, ophthalmologists have a blinding or two during their careers, and general surgeons have a few fatal and near-fatal cases yearly. No one can predict disasters, and good surgeons never consider themselves entirely blameless.

Studies of liposuction surgeons show that they puncture their patients' internal organs about once every 3,000 cases. In some areas of the body, changing the angle of the suction cannula by fifteen (15) degrees does it. Some of these cases are serious, and others are never noticed. Possibly ten percent of symptomatic punctures die. Since a typical liposuction requires two thousand strokes of the instrument, surgeons who have performed 1000 cases have completed two million cannula strokes. Given these numbers, perfect coordination and consistency are impossible.

Cassandra's Memo

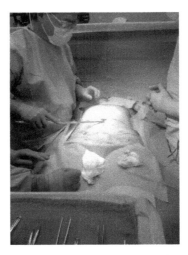

Notice the liposuction cannula in Dr. Mangubat's hand.

Patients sign documents saying complications and death are possible, but who expects anything to happen? No one wants to hear about that paperwork in the hospital after their bowel repair. I know doctors who will swear under oath (for a price, of course) that punctures are malpractice and should never happen. We performed over 10,000 liposuction cases in my surgical centers, and I have seen this problem several times. Fortunately, none of my patients ever died—from this, anyway.

I often meditate about the following. Hippocrates told us to do no harm, but risks are everywhere. We must take full responsibility in an era when bad outcomes are inevitably viewed as malpractice.

* * *

Climbing has obvious risks. Our safety rules are simple, but like surgeons, we are imperfect. I had five friends who made errors that resulted in spectacular contact with the ground after falls of sixty to 3000 feet. Tying a bad knot might be all it takes for it to happen. No amount of checking cuts your chance of this error to zero or guarantees that you will even tie a knot.

I once climbed at Riverside Quarry using a rope but without a partner holding it for me (these "rope soloing" techniques are beyond the scope of this article). When I was at the anchor, a hundred feet up, I attempted to tie a knot that I had used thousands of times before:

I tied the slip knot above. It should have been the "figure 8" below:

Cassandra's Memo

I then slid back down the rope using a "Grigri" friction device on the left-hand strand. If I had used the right-hand rope, I would have died. After I got to the bottom, I climbed back up the rock using the rope for safety but without putting my weight on it. When I was once more at the top, I realized that the knot was not secure and that I might have killed myself. I was shaken but had to presence of mind to tie myself in and take the photo. Since I did not slip, I thought, "No harm, no foul." I retied the knot and carried on.

Here is another example with consequences. I was on a speed ascent of Yosemite's El Capitan (for me, this meant less than 24 hours). I was climbing despite crippling professional stresses (error 1). My partner convinced me, against my better judgment, to bring only one long rope instead of two (mistake 2). He got ahead of me and used too much rope (error 3), so when I had to do a maneuver called a "pendulum," I did not have enough extra rope at my end (mistake 4). I slammed into the rock and broke my foot.

We rappelled down, and I crawled a mile to the road. When I went to see my orthopedist the next week, he cast my foot but did not refer me to a specialist (mistake 5).

He told me to wait three months, and I listened to him

instead of getting another opinion (mistake 6). The specialist I saw later said that waiting caused a "malunion" or improper healing. If I had seen him within ten days, he could have repaired the problem, and I would have been fine. This string of six errors resulted in a permanent injury that does not allow me much hiking and sings painful songs to me daily.

I was later successful with Hans Florine.

I climbed many dozens of times a year when I was active. I was careful, even paranoid, worked on my skills, and prevented thousands of mishaps. For example, I recognized and avoided loose holds. While climbing easy ground a hundred feet off the ground without a rope, I slipped on wet rock but caught myself. And once I avoided falling 40 feet by screaming STOP to my belayer. He had nearly let my belay rope slide through the device he was holding. With so many experiences like these, I gave little thought to mistakes that did not result in harm. But once in many hundreds of climbing days, fatigue or a minor distraction causes an accident.

Never fall prey to thinking that training, ritual, and careful technique will prevent all calamities. Something will eventually get you if you expose yourself to life's risks—unexpected troubles are inevitable. For climbers, surgeons, and all of us, errors are the price we pay for living full lives. Do not fool yourself—it will happen to you.

Be careful out there.

Part Seven

Every Psych Drug Damages the Brain

Chapter 29
Antidepressants are the Root Cause of Mass Shootings

Who can protest and does not is an accomplice in the act.

— Talmud

Occam's Razor states that one or a few causes for a problem are far more likely than many. The primary culprit for mass shootings is obvious, even when viewed through the media attempts to blame guns.

Although masks, lockdowns, and other frustrations must contribute to mass shootings, the noxious "selective serotonin reuptake inhibitors" (SSRIs) have been proven to cause murder and suicide since they were first studied in the 1980s. Over ten percent of Americans take them. Murdermeds.com* and antidepressantstatistics.com give powerful testimony that they are the primary reason for the violence wave. *This website is down but can be accessed on the Wayback machine HERE.

Robert Yoho, MD (ret)

SUBSTACK LINK

* * *

Mobster Pharma companies promote SSRI antidepressants. They were FDA-approved because the pharmaceutical industry paid half the Agency's budget during the patent approval process, turning the corporations into FDA *clients*. For more details about the drug manufacturers' culpability, see A Midwestern Doctor's Substack essay HERE.

The following description of the antidepressant disaster was first published in my 2020 book, *Butchered by "Health-care,"* Amazon link HERE. It has over 300 five-star reviews.

> Wendy Dolin learned the hard way about antidepres-
> sants. Her husband, Stewart, threw himself in front of a
> train a week after he started taking generic Paxil. Mr.
> Dolin's doctors gave him the drug for job-related anxiety,
> but it creates intolerable restlessness in three to five
> percent of people using it. He was last seen pacing back
> and forth on the train platform.
>
> He killed himself despite what his family thought
> was a perfect life. His two grown children adored him,
> and he loved his career, travel, skiing, and work. He was
> happily married to his high school sweetheart. When

Cassandra's Memo

Ms. Dolin sued the drug company, testimony established that it had hidden Paxil-related suicides.

For two decades, while making billions of dollars, the manufacturer had been quietly settling thousands of similar cases. In 2017, Ms. Dolin won a three million dollar judgment. Her attorneys had spent millions, but the company filed an appeal. It claimed that the original manufacturer was not responsible for subsequent generic versions of the medication.

David Carmichael's story [featured in the next chapter] is worse. He took Paxil for two periods of several months each and felt suicidal each time. His doctor advised him that increasing his dose would decrease his stress. When he did, he went from suicidal to homicidal and killed his 11-year-old son. The circumstances indicted Paxil, and Mr. Carmichael believes it was the cause. Since blaming the drug was impractical for his legal defense, this was not brought up at his trial. The court acquitted him of murder because he was judged to be temporarily psychotic, which means out of touch with reality.

SSRIstories.org has about 5000 first-hand news stories about situations like these. The drug companies claim that the drugs are bystanders and that the perpetrators are prone to violence. A half-hour spent on this website makes a compelling case that the drugs are the cause (this excerpt is continued at the above link).

Chapter 30
My Most Painful, Pitiful, and Dramatic Interview

My behavior when taking Paxil was calm, organized, and homicidal—just like the school shooters.

— David Carmichael

This is about a man who became psychotic under the influence of an antidepressant and murdered his son. The post below is reprinted from the MadInAmerica.com article HERE.

SUBSTACK LINK for my interview with David

Cassandra's Memo

Every time I read about another school shooting, or a mass killing like the Germanwings plane crash, my heart breaks because I know they might have been prevented if the public was better educated about the rare but potentially lethal side effects of the antidepressants that many mass killers were taking.

There is little doubt in my mind that many school shooters were in an antidepressant-induced state of psychosis, which is a loss of contact with reality that makes it difficult to distinguish between what is real and what is not real.

That's what happened to me.

My life before antidepressants was a good one. I had a beautiful family with two children, Gillian and Ian, and a fun-loving home in Toronto, Canada. Children from around the neighborhood would come to play at our house — we had a fitness studio in the basement and a half pipe, trampoline and climbing wall in the backyard. Ian, his friends and other neighborhood children would spend hours riding their BMX bikes on our half pipe.

Meanwhile, I had a successful career as a physical activity and sport consultant. Then, at 44 years of age, I started to worry about cash flow issues in July of 2003, toward the end of a recession. I had lost weight, started to shake in the shower and had difficulty sleeping, so I went to my family doctor who prescribed the selective serotonin re-uptake inhibitor (SSRI) Paxil to me without explaining any side effects. When I first started taking Paxil, I had suicidal thoughts but they disappeared after about a week and I was able to secure several work contracts. By September, I was feeling mentally healthy again. After forgetting to take Paxil for a few days in February 2004, I weaned myself off the drug over several weeks.

In July of 2004 I started to experience the same symptoms that I had in July of 2003, but this time it was caused by sleep deprivation from juggling so many contracts. I was better able to manage the contracts while on Paxil, possibly because (looking back) I was probably manic for most of the 8 months that I was on the drug from July 2003 to February 2004.

On July 8, 2004, I put myself back on 40 mg of Paxil daily, using the supply that I had when I started to wean myself off the drug in February.

A few days after I started taking Paxil again, I was having suicidal thoughts. I thought I could get rid of the thoughts and recover more quickly if I increased my dosage to what I read was the maximum therapeutic level in the Guide to Drugs in Canada, published by the Canadian Pharmacists Association. It would be like taking 2 aspirin instead of 1 to get rid of a headache.

On July 16, I started taking 60 mg of Paxil a day. Three days later, I planned my suicide. Then I went from planning my suicide to planning a murder-suicide to planning a murder.

On July 31, I took the life of my 11-year-old son Ian in a London, Canada hotel room and was charged with first-degree murder. My motivation was based on a type of psychosis called delusions (fixed false beliefs) that I had at the time. I was convinced, in my delusional state, that out of love for my family, it would be best for me to take Ian's life and to sacrifice my own life by spending the next 25 years in prison. I thought that:

1. Ian had permanent brain damage because he had mild epilepsy, which I was never concerned about when I wasn't delusional or I would not

have encouraged him to try difficult tricks on his BMX. Autopsy results from the London police showed there was nothing wrong with Ian's brain.

2. Ian was in a living hell because he was teased every so often by other children because of a minor learning disability. This was never a concern of mine when I wasn't delusional. He was a late-developing child born in December, which are the youngest children in their classrooms in Canadian schools.

3. Ian was going to kill his sister Gillian because they were arguing. Gillian was 14 years old at the time and when I wasn't delusional, I wasn't concerned about what was simply normal sibling interactive behavior.

4. My wife was going to have a nervous breakdown caring for Ian because of what I thought, in my delusional state, was his permanent brain damage and being in a living hell.

5. Ian was going to hurt other children because he had pushed a child into the swimming pool at a summer day camp in Toronto that I was directing, a few days before I took his life.

Although none of these delusions make any sense to me today, they were real toward the end of July 2004 and lasted until the middle of August 2004, when my delusional mind was returning to normal while I was on suicide watch in a London, Ontario jail.

The planning that you see in many of the school shootings, and the calmness of the shooters, is similar to my own behavior after being on Paxil for three weeks in July 2004, which I've described in this RxISK blog post. The mass killers were probably suffering from delusions and were functioning at high intellectual levels, like me.

Ten days after I took Ian's life, while I was still psychotic, my criminal defence lawyer had a team of medical specialists assess me to help build the defense that I was not criminally responsible (NCR) for first-degree murder because I was suffering from major depression at the time, which was supported by anecdotal evidence that the London Police collected from my family, friends and colleagues.

None of the test results supported the argument that I was NCR so my criminal lawyer didn't use them as part of my defense.

- I was not in a major depression according to my results from the Minnesota Multiphasic Personality Inventory (MMPI).
- My concentration was high, which is contrary to one of the major indicators of major depression (diminished ability to think or concentrate). I completed the MMPI, which had more than 500 multiple choice questions, in about 45 minutes. Comparatively, when I was being assessed at the Royal Ottawa Mental Health Centre in early November 2004 after not being properly treated for my major depression for 4 months at the London Middlesex Detention Centre and in the worst depressive state of my life, it took me about 3.5 hours over 2 days to complete the MMPI with

the results indicating that I was in a major depression.

- I scored very high on an IQ test, probably much higher than normal, which is contrary to being in a major depression.
- A forensic psychiatrist could not report that I was psychotic at the time. My delusions were still strong for about 14 days after I took Ian's life and stopped taking Paxil.

Although none of the test results made sense to my criminal lawyer or myself in 2004, they make sense now. The *Compendium of Pharmaceuticals and Specialties*, a prescription drug reference for doctors and other health professionals published by the Canadian Pharmacists Association, which contains drug monographs provided by pharmaceutical companies, listed delusions and psychosis as rare side effects of Paxil (1 in 1,000) at least as far back as 1996. GlaxoSmithKline, the manufacturer of Paxil, would have provided this information.

Before my trial I was diagnosed by two forensic psychiatrists, one hired by my criminal lawyer and the other by the crown attorney, as being in a "major depression with psychotic episodes" when I took Ian's life. This resulted in the judgment that I was "not criminally responsible on account of a mental disorder."

Paxil was never built into my defense during the criminal trial. Even though there was some indication before my trial that Paxil might have caused my psychosis, my lawyer told me how difficult it would be to prove causation, and even if we were successful at proving that Paxil was the probable cause of my homicidal psychotic episode, the best I could expect was a manslaughter conviction since prescription drugs were in the same intoxication section of the Criminal Code of Canada as illicit drugs. Since we already had expert reports to support our NCR defense, we decided not to build Paxil into my defense.

There's no doubt among the more than a dozen forensic psychiatrists I have seen that I was psychotic when I took Ian's life in July 2004. What a jury in a civil lawsuit that I filed against GlaxoSmithKline in October 2011 will now have to determine is whether my psychosis was caused by a mental disorder or Paxil.

I never had a mental disorder before being prescribed Paxil for the first time in 2003 at 44 years of age, and I haven't had a mental disorder while being off all medications since 2010.

The combination of the common side effect of emotional blunting and the rare side effect of delusions was the probable cause of my calm, organized, homicidal behavior.

To help prevent school shootings and other mass killings, it's time for GlaxoSmithKline and other pharmaceutical companies to publicly acknowledge that antidepressants can cause potentially lethal psychotic episodes in rare cases.

For more about Mr. Carmichael, see knowyourdrugs.org, HERE, and HERE. To help Mr. Carmichael spread the word about these vile medications, donate HERE. For a video about a mass murder related to SSRIs, see HERE.

Chapter 31
Ben Bathen Was Butchered by Psychiatry

B
en is a brilliant computer engineer who once worked as a Google contractor. His problems started in his mid-20s when an 80-hour-a-week programming job stressed him. A psychologist pressured him to take medications, and although he did not like the idea, after some convincing, he gave in. She sent him to a physician for prescribing but continued to counsel him about the various drugs.

Ben moved 3000 miles away to the East coast. The psychologist continued charging Ben for monthly phone calls but never saw him for the next decade. Her Ph.D. license did not cover advising about medications, but in her defense, psychiatrists say exactly the same thing.

Ben developed tardive dyskinesia with spastic movements, which is brain damage. It has become chronic but is fortunately mild. According to the medical industry's marketing, SSRIs and related drugs almost never cause problems. But these medications eventually made Ben psychotic, meaning he could not tell what was real. His behavior deteriorated, and he left threatening phone messages for the psychologist.

SUBSTACK LINK RUMBLE

Even though Ben was on the other side of the US and posed no physical threat, the psychologist managed to get him arrested for threatening her. Ben spent two years in prison before he understood that the drugs were responsible for his behavior. When he got out, he took a $50 genetic test ("cytochrome P-450" DNA) that proved his body could not process antidepressants properly. People with this result are vulnerable to severe drug reactions like Ben's, but the test is not used as a routine before starting people on these drugs.

Ben eventually read many sources I used for *Butchered by "Healthcare."* He found that his story was far from unique and learned that psychiatric drugs have never been properly compared with sugar-pill "controls." This means that there is no proof that they work.

Ben trusted his doctors and believed they were competent, but the entire experience was disastrous, and he is now a convicted felon. The only good thing to happen was that Ben was forced to withdraw from all medications while in prison. Pharma marketing says SSRIs are not addictive, but he learned the hard way that quitting them is far more brutal and lengthy than stopping opioids. It was miserable, and he has not touched drugs like these since.

He still has the spastic condition. The website about his experiences is wrongfulssriconvictions.com. Listen to the interview for more.

Psychiatrists believe their drugs are effective and non-toxic. But you do not have to be a Google engineer to learn this is a pack of lies. After his experiences, Ben knew that he must make his own judgments about healthcare and not rely much on doctors.

This LINK will allow you to listen to the related chapter of *Butchered by "Healthcare,"* The ebook is $4.00 on Kindle.

Chapter 32
Suzanne was Kidnapped by Incompetent Psychiatrists

She escaped a locked mental hospital and was "recalled to life." This phrase is from *A Tale of Two Cities* by Charles Dickens.

SUBSTACK LINK

Suzanne took Paxil, a drug related to Prozac, for six years. No doctor warned her that these "selective serotonin reuptake inhibitors" (SSRIs) cause brain damage. When her psychiatrist tried to wean her off the medication, she began to have sexual dysfunction and other withdrawal symptoms. So he recommended restarting 10 mg daily, a low dose.

Noxious, menacing effects may occur when a patient stops or restarts SSRIs. After Suzanne began retaking Paxil, she became paranoid and had violent verbal outbursts. She also started getting involuntary spastic movements (dystonia, torticollis, or possibly tardive dyskinesia). She became suicidal, fantasized about cutting herself, and could not stop thinking about violence. These are all well-known, occasional effects of SSRIs.

Her doctors forcibly hospitalized her, and since her family had little understanding or other options, they went along. She was soon hallucinating and repeatedly screaming nonsense words. She wanted to hurt the people around her and had to be physically restrained.

Her doctors increased the Paxil to 30 mg daily—triple the initial dosage that caused the problems. Although this made Suzanne worse, they added Zyprexa (an antipsychotic), Ativan (a sedative), and Ambien (a sleep drug). She says Zyprexa gave her a sensation like knives stabbing all over her body. It also produced thoughts about people trying to kill her. She was held in a prison-like locked mental health facility, and the staff threatened to increase her doses if she did not improve.

Since these effects occurred immediately after the dosage changes, she realized the drugs were to blame. Suzanne began putting her medications under her tongue to spit them out later. She also started studying 14 hours a day using her cell phone. This became her salvation. She read first in Dutch and later found an English language Facebook group dedicated to "akathisia," her primary drug side effect.

She discovered MISSD.CO, Woodymatters.com, MadinAmerica.com, and other websites dedicated to psychiatric medication disasters like hers. Katinka Blackford-Newmann's story dumbfounded Suzanne because their involuntary hospitalizations were nearly identical.

Suzanne deteriorated mentally and physically and developed severe insomnia. When she tried to explain akathisia and dystonia to her state-employed Dutch psychiatrists, they insisted that there was no such thing. They also told her she must stop researching, or they would never release her, and threatened to take her cell phone.

Suzanne learned how to video-call people in the Facebook akathisia group and contacted Ben Bathen (last chapter). She popped up on his computer in the middle of his afternoon and said, "I have akathisia, it is horrible, and I do not want any more Paxil!!! Can you get me out of here?"

After his research, Ben had the emails of activists and doctors trying to help pharmaceutical company victims. Several worldwide experts on adverse drug effects, including Peter Goetszche and Dick Bijl, responded to his inquiries. Ben also contacted David Healy and Selma Eikelenboom. They communicated with Suzanne by email, then phone calls, and finally found a doctor who helped her.

She was released within a few weeks and successfully tapered herself off almost all medication, although she said her Ativan addiction was particularly agonizing. She occasionally calls Ben at three AM her (European) time because of severe, persistent insomnia.

Although Suzanne was traumatized by her experience, since leaving the hospital, she recovered rapidly. Although she sometimes wonders how to return to everyday life after such an experience, she is back to being an attractive, well-adjusted 29-year-old schoolteacher. She attempts to repair her damaged family relationships and sometimes worries about the patients she left behind in the hospital.

No doctor ever took responsibility for Suzanne's nightmare or apologized to her.

Notes

From *Butchered by "Healthcare"* (2021):

> The Selective Serotonin Re-uptake Inhibitor (SSRI) name was pseudoscience dreamed up in SmithKline Beecham's marketing department. The 'chemical imbalance in the brain' idea was the brainstorm of a sales copywriter in the 1950s. Knowledge of serotonin and other neurotransmitters was even more sketchy when Prozac was invented than now. Today, this seductive but mythical gibberish embarrasses researchers.

Akathisia is a sometimes unbearable agitation during psychiatric drug usage, withdrawal, or dosage change. Some victims of this syndrome attempt suicide or become violent. This can also occur with Reglan (metoclopramide), a drug used for gastrointestinal problems. More from *Butchered by "Healthcare:"*

> "Typical" or first-generation antipsychotics such as Thorazine and Haldol have been marketed as a treatment for insanity since the 1950s, but they have terrible side effects. These include involuntary movements that look like Parkinson's disease. Rigid muscles with painful spasms are also frequent. Akathisia, an uncontrollable restlessness that occasionally results in suicide, occurs in 25 percent. The neuroleptic malignant syndrome, a violent body temperature elevation, is rare but life-threatening.

Tardive dyskinesia (TD) is the best known of these problems. Twenty to thirty percent of people taking these drugs get it, and 500,000 individuals in the US have it. Involuntary movements are characteristic. Patients' tongues, arms, and legs may make strange motions. Their cheeks, jaws, and noses contort. Eyelids spasm, eyes move around, and the patients may make unintentional sounds. The psychiatrists call these "worm-tongue, fly-tongue, or rabbit-face." Caregivers may never recognize the drug(s) as the cause and may blame and punish patients.

TD usually occurs after six months to two years of treatment but may happen after just a few months. When the drugs are discontinued, the syndrome often lingers, or sometimes it begins for the first time. Many patients who use these medications must continue because this effect often worsens without them. The brain's grey matter shrinks, which is proof of damage. TD is also associated with premature death. (Note: Ben Bathen has some remaining tardive dyskinesia symptoms after his harrowing experience with the psychiatric industry.)

Antipsychotics destroy physical health. They are linked to stroke, seizure, weight gain, blood clots, heart attacks, pancreatitis, and heart rhythm disturbance. There has never been a recall by the FDA, only a black-box warning.

The newer "atypical" antipsychotics include Abilify and Zyprexa, which have been available since the 1990s. Their marketing proclaimed that they produced less TD and other related damage because the initial studies claimed that the tardive dyskinesia rate was a quarter of that for older medications. Later trials focusing on TD revealed little substantial difference between the older and newer drugs.

Like the first generation, the atypical antipsychotics cause health problems: stroke, blood clots, weight gain, heart attacks, and diabetes. They cut up to twenty years off patients' lives and shrink the brain. Eli Lilly, the developer, concealed these adverse effects, although they knew about them from the first trials.

Any psychiatrist who does not immediately recognize the signs and symptoms of these drug effects is incompetent.

Chapter 33
Psychiatrists Should Be Abolished Along With Their Drugs

D r. Patrick Hahn agrees with me about this. Psychotherapy and "analysis" are unproven and rife with abuse, but the drugs are worse.

Psychiatry is our most expensive and harmful medical sector. Unlike other specialties, no sign, scan, blood test, or physical finding is diagnostic for any "mental health disease." Third-world countries, which cannot afford our toxic drugs, have far better outcomes. This is because the medicines cause—and render chronic—many of the conditions they are purported to treat.

Talking therapy is safer but frequently abusive. Authorities, including Peter Goetzsche (HERE), have shown evidence that it is more effective than pills. But this is a low standard, for the medications are actively damaging.

Psychiatrists overdose even our precious children.

SUBSTACK LINK

Dr. Hahn convinced me that even the worst psychiatric conditions, such as schizophrenia, are closely related to environmental factors like child abuse. None of them have proven genetic influences. Overwhelming research shows that these issues, like developmental disorders, respond to love, kindness, and human contact. Hahn says that calling these "diseases" confuses them with body illness with physical signs and symptoms.

Despite this, the accepted orthodoxy is that these conditions are biological or genetic. Since this is without backing, no justification exists for prescribing toxic, brain-damaging medications. But justify it, the psychiatrists do. They concocted and enshrined thousands of diagnoses in their *Diagnostic and Statistical Manual of Mental Disorders* (DSM) to support their actions. Here is how I describe this book in Butchered by "Healthcare."

> The DSM is a kind of chaotic bible used to promote mental diseases. With its code numbers used for insurance, some call it the billing bible. Created primarily by psychiatrists on industry payroll, it mutates and metastasizes every few years through a vote of the APA [American Psychiatric Association] members. In 2017, after many editions, it was 947 pages long.
>
> Insiders have decried its intellectual disarray for decades. It has become the perverse standard in the service of drug marketing.

Putting names on vague clusters of symptoms serves the sole purpose of deluding psychiatrists and their victims into thinking the pseudoscience is real. But it is entirely soap bubbles that are blown up to justify pretensions, doctors' incomes, and Pharma revenues—and not in that order. Prescriptions of obscenely expensive, brain-damaging psychiatric drugs are the result.

Like vaccines, no psych drug has ever been appropriately studied using sugar pills or saline controls.

Talking therapy

If you have any connection with counseling, psychotherapy, or psychoanalysis, *Final Analysis: The Making and Unmaking of a Psychoanalyst** (1998) by Jeffrey Masson will alter your perceptions. It is a timeless, powerful, and beautifully written indictment of Freudian psychoanalysis. He shows this is ineffective and rife with patient sexual and emotional abuse. The system was designed for the analysts' benefit. He says:

As I look back on my training, I can see that much of it was an indoctrination process, a means of socializing me in a certain direction; it was partly intellectual, partly political, and even to some extent had to do with class. The guild mattered more than anything else. If this process was successful, it became almost impossible to question any of the major ideas within the parent organization...

What I was searching for, and what psychoanalysis promises, cannot in fact be given by another person, cannot be found in a theory or a profession, no matter how well-meaning. It is only, I am convinced, to be had or not had, through living. There are no experts in loving, no scholars of living, no doctors of human emotions, and no gurus of the soul. But we need not be alone; friendship is a precious gift, and all that we need do to see is remove the blinders...

Masson describes abuses:

I learned that Alan Parkin... who had been the president of the Toronto Psychoanalytic Institute and of the Canadian Psychoanalytic Society, and even a vice president the International Psychoanalytical Association, had voluntarily given up his medical license rather than face accusations, from several psychoanalytic female patients, that he sexually abused them during office hours (and charged for the sessions!)...

"Professional" talking treatment by people with the pretenses of psychiatric and psychological degrees works no better than contact with clergy. HERE is one reference about this among many. Another source HERE questions the most accepted talk method, Cognitive Behavioral Therapy.

I have a personal punch line—in my 30s, I was a

251

believer. During that decade, I awkwardly dog-paddled through on-the-couch psychoanalysis. I was never physically abused by my "care provider," but we spent many expensive hours discussing his conviction that I had shagged my mother. Since I had no recall, he claimed this was a "repressed memory."

It was the era of the Los Angeles McMartin cases. Toddlers in daycare were urged to fabricate stories about hidden basements where caregivers abused and tortured them. Prosecutors put some of the preschool staff in prison for years. These theories have been discredited—no Holocaust survivor, for example, has ever been proven to have forgotten their experiences.

To use the woke parlance, I am a "survivor" of this oddball trend. My wife laughs at this characterization. She says I was crazy and my shrink a conman.

The following is from the Introduction to Planet Psych chapter at the start of the psychiatry section of *Butchered*. I describe the drug disasters in other chapters.

Most physicians view psychiatrists as somewhat feral animals. We suspect—with some justification—that many of their ideas are hot air. Unlike any other specialty, psychiatrists care for people with normal labs and radiologic tests. They keep only patients with purely subjective problems and pass patients with "organic" issues, such as thyroid disease, to others. These are the people with identifiable physical signs, symptoms, and tests. Likewise, psychiatrists base treatment outcomes on their theories and observations of patient behavior rather than measurable, objective results.

No other specialty has a sizable group of protesters who oppose their legitimacy. These include not only

Scientologists but psychologists, scientists, journalists, and a few renegade psychiatrists. These "psychiatry deniers" believe that most psychiatric drugs used today are harmful, ineffective, and vastly overprescribed. They question the specialty's power to lock people up and force them to take damaging medications based only on their opinions...

Mainstream psychiatrists believe the four primary drug categories they use—stimulants, SSRIs (Selective Serotonin Re-uptake Inhibitors), benzodiazepines, and antipsychotics—are effective, beneficial, and cause little harm. Citing their close-range experience treating mental illness, they claim that these diseases are under-treated and that even patients with mild symptoms should take medications. Their studies and standards support this. But these are so structurally compromised and biased with industry money that they are useless.

These "psychoactive" medications influence sleep, wakefulness, mood, behavior, and so forth. Unlike most drugs, they enter the brain by crossing the blood-brain barrier, a natural microscopic defense against toxins. Drugs that behave like this can alter or damage the entire central nervous system. Although these medications are commonly used and casually prescribed, taking them is a trap because addiction is common and frequently irreversible...

Patrick D. Hahn, Ph.D., is an Affiliate Professor of Biology at Loyola University Maryland and has two Master's degrees and a Ph.D. in biology. He works outside of healthcare and makes no money from it or his books about it. He is a neutral observer who sees these issues through his biological background. This gives him deep credibility, particularly because his humanist conclusions are at odds with his training in genetics.

Dr. Hahn is the author of Obedience Pills: ADHD and the Medicalization of Childhood (2022), Prescription for Sorrow: Antidepressants, Suicide, and Violence (2020), and Madness and Genetic Determinism: Is Mental Illness in Our Genes? (2019). He writes at Mad In America and at patrickdhahn.substack.com.

Chapter 34
Diversion: Gut-Checking the People I Meet

Most people don't believe something can happen until it already has. It's not stupidity or weakness; it's just human nature.

— Brad Pitt's character in the *World War* Z movie.

W e are facing zombies now—people who can't see the overwhelming evidence before their eyes. I have lost a lot of dear friends to this, for I have given up listening to circular arguments and suffering never-ending debates with people who quote the media gaslighting. (Pass me a chainsaw.)

In this chapter, I am at a middle-class resort, trotting around collecting people's emails, measuring their awareness, and grinning like a Mormon missionary.

I added a couple of blue-eyed Swedes, then bummed a cigarette from a man who cleans cars for Avis. He told me Jesus would save us but gave me his email anyway. A smug

Swiss claimed that he knew a lot, then opened his mouth and proved he was clueless. A football coach with a handshake that brutalized mine challenged me to summarize the situation for him, and I thought, "Why not?"

I told him that the prime movers were the bankers. They embezzle from us by inflating our money, which has been going on for centuries. As each currency is destroyed, they repeat the process using a new one. They are now trying to destabilize the dollar. Their goal is to institute digital currency to give them control and allow their thievery to continue.

Coach hadn't heard anything like this before, but he graciously said, "Interesting. Put me on your list." He had hurt my hand, so after I got his email, I went in for a second handshake and snatched his fingertips. I showed him I could frog-walk him around the room if I wanted. He was a big guy with an iron grip, but he told me later he was 87. I felt like an idiot and apologized.

As I took the intellectual temperature around me, I realized:

1. Most people had no more awareness or curiosity than our vaccine-damaged autistic kids.
2. I could not explain jack s**t in 3 minutes.

So I thought about the problem for a few days. I realized that people go through certain stages as they wake up to current events. These are, in rough order:

Level 0 people have a vague idea that something is wrong but believe "everybody's opinion is valuable."

Level 1 understands that both the coronavirus and the "vaccine" are fraudulent.

Level 2 understands that these are manufactured bioweapons used to weaken us, kill us, and destroy our fertility. (The full effects of the vax will not be fully known for years, but the high estimates are that tens to hundreds of millions will eventually die. Other calculations are less pessimistic.)

Level 3 understands big tech's wall of censorship that, among other distortions, concealed early treatments for Covid. These would have saved millions of lives.

Level 4 knows the chains of evidence proving the conspirators' guilt for:

- Fauci
- Gates
- The Chinese Communist Party
- Soros and other crazy billionaires
- Globalists/World Economic Forum plants inside our governments
- Tech companies
- Politicians from both political parties. Democrats are the worst.

Level 5 knows that our peace of mind is being attacked from many angles using psychological warfare deployed by federal agencies and the media. These include but are not limited to the following:

- "Carbon dioxide is bad for the earth." (It is good for life, and the concentration in our atmosphere is now one of the lowest levels recorded over hundreds of millions of years. We are not far above the threshold that would kill plant life.)

- Transsexual "normalizing." (The tranny insanity is promoted by corporate criminals rather than this small, weak, and disturbed group of people.)
- Pedophilia normalizing.
- Black Lives Matter. These racist ideas were fabricated to incite hate. Soros pays ANTIFA criminals to keep this going, and he also works to defund the police. And he contributes to the election of prosecutors who ignore our laws.
- The claim that vegan diets are the most healthy and "good for the planet." (Both ideas are wrong. See the diet chapter in *Hormone Secrets*.)
- Possibly the most obvious gaslighting is an attempt to normalize cannibalism and eating bugs! See HERE.
- The claim that Russia is a threat to the US and the Ukraine war is a real, not a manufactured, situation.

Level 6 understands that vital US foundations are under attack and compromised, including:

- The US Constitution and its Amendments. (The best summaries are RFK's lectures on the Children's Health Defense website.)
- Our universities and public schools have become insanely expensive sewers taken over by zombies spreading woke propaganda.

- Three huge investment funds are majority owners of Pfizer and Moderna. Their investments total over 25 trillion dollars. One of these funds, BlackRock, controls over 10% of the world economy and over 90% of the media. Their website says, "We are committed to diversity, equity and inclusion (DEI) across every level of our firm and within every region and country where we operate." DEI is a barely concealed DIE. They advocate genocidal population reduction.
- **Level 7s** understand that we face psychopaths without human sensibilities. Gates and many others are aggressive and irrational; their goal is to kill or injure us. Profits are secondary.

Level 8s realize that at least a third of our population is hypnotized by propaganda and almost unreachable.

Level 9s understand that our healthcare is ruinous and that many harms and fatalities are baked into its standard practices. They also understand that US regulatory agencies and medical journals are on the payroll and working against patients and stability.

Level 10s know that the prime movers are the central bankers.

If you understand the above, you live with me in a house of pain and anger. We know that we must keep fighting no matter what happens. We can never unlearn, forget, or forgive.

I finally concluded that three minutes of badgering strangers was useless and that, sooner or later, it would get me smacked. But because my emails explain the whole thing, I still prospect for subscribers.

Reading *The Real Anthony Fauci* brings a few people to reason. You can gift it as a Kindle ebook for $3.

Eisenhower said, "Pessimism never won any battles." He resolved to take any negativity he felt to his pillow at night. We must do the same.

Part Eight

Transgenderism Poisons
Minds and Bodies

Chapter 35
I Must Have Been Asleep at the Start of the Transgender Debacle

Some ideas are so stupid that only intellectuals believe them.

— George Orwell

I rreversible Damage, The Transgender Craze Seducing Our Daughters (2021), by Abigail Shrier, has over 6,000 Amazon reviews averaging 4.5 stars. It describes some of the events I somehow missed over the last five years. It is engaging, poetically written, and an overwhelming indictment of the malignant absurdity of believing that sexes are a "social construct."

The book is not about adult men who consider themselves women or the reverse. It is not about gays or lesbians. It is about an attack on our most psychologically vulnerable group—adolescent and preadolescent girls. Shrier's style is not overly judgmental, but I cannot write with her objectivity.

SUBSTACK LINK

Current social media celebrates the transgender (TS/TG) wave. YouTube "influencers" and TS center "caregivers" say that if anyone notices feelings of this kind, they should act on them. Preadolescent girls are susceptible to all sorts of ideas like these.

The process typically begins with stress or trauma—divorce, rejection, a family breakup, or perhaps something minor. Everyone has dramas, and young women feel them acutely. Next, with the help of social media "influencers" on YouTube channels, these children are trained to believe the whole thing is plausible. TS is a thrill of rebellion and a new identity, which is seductive for some young girls. Exploring sex earlier, which has many disadvantages, might clarify these feelings, but these victims are most often virgins.

First, the groomers encourage the use of breast binders that disguise developing sexuality. These are tight, irritating, worsen asthma, and occasionally crack delicate ribs. They often make developing breasts permanently saggy and flat. Binders are used, typically without parental knowledge, and at every stage, the "counselors" goad their targets to separate emotionally from their parents.

"Puberty blocker" medications such as Lupron follow. These toxic, injectable drugs are conventionally used to treat women's infertility or prostate cancer in older men.

Everyone feels terrible when taking them, and they can create irreversible brain damage.

Testosterone abuse is the next step. "Gender clinic" doctors prescribe adult male doses. This produces blood levels that are ten to twenty times those of an average woman. Over a few months, the young girls' faces and bodies assume masculine shapes, and their vaginas shrink and dry. Uteruses atrophy and frequently cramp. Voices deepen, clitorises become huge and protrude, and infertility is universal. Ordinary sex becomes difficult and irritating; for many, orgasm is impossible. Most of these effects are permanent.

These adolescents are then encouraged to undergo "top surgery," a euphemism for getting their breasts sliced off. The resulting nipple is either low or better-centered but numb. Cosmetic results depend on the surgeon's skill, but in all cases, an unnatural horizontal scar remains.

Some victims have their wombs and ovaries cut out. A few get their enlarged clitorises altered to pass urine through them and to appear more like penises. This proce-dure involves cutting a graft of skin, fat, nerve, and artery from the forearm, which leaves a disfiguring scar. If the surgery is botched—which happens with some regularity—the entire area of the original clitoris may die and heal into a numb scar.

Most and sometimes all of these procedures can now be undertaken with little or no psychological counseling or parental involvement. These children can usually obtain a prescription for Lupron or testosterone from a poorly super-vised college "healthcare" clinic. Since the Affordable Care Act ("Obamacare") was passed, birth control pills and other hormones—even these—have been covered by insurance.

Shrier's book has story after heart-rending story about

the kids, their parents, and the tragic people running the YouTube channels. These girls ("transitioned" to boys) have extra hair, deep voices, and enlarged clitorises, but they still retain a feminine delicacy. Their identities are fragile, for they are neither male nor female.

Insurance companies generously reimburse these doctors. Although these procedures are the only cosmetic surgeries that permanently alter function, the surgeons mainly function as technicians rather than carefully considering each patient. No one is in charge of this asylum except the media "influencers" and those they have groomed.

This process does not relieve emotional pain or poor adjustment, for the telling hallmark of the TG "community" in adults and children is attempted suicide. The incidence in many studies is 40 percent, and the rate is the same before and after transitioning. One transexual commented, "There's so much depression, self-harm, and drug abuse in the trans community. They're all goddam miserable... it's just like this misery fest."

Many who try to become men before 20 switch back and later "identify" as women. But they are never entirely feminine again, and few ever achieve fertility. Nothing works to satisfactorily correct breast removal. Breast augmentation creates cold, firm, and unnatural results because no breast tissue remains to cover the implant.

America has a long history of destructive fads based on young women's hysteria. The Salem witch trials were one. More recently, the McMartin-type recovered memories theories sent a lot of caretakers to jail based on imaginary stories told by juveniles. This phantom-memory idea has since been discredited, and almost all of the accused were eventually released. Some psychologists believe that youth

TG syndromes are related to multiple personality disorder, a disease that some also categorize as hysteria.

The number of adult transgenders is well under one percent of the population, but since peer pressure may influence the younger ones to convert in groups, there are many more juveniles.

Many adult gays and lesbians—and mature transgenders—see this trend as a fraud, speak out against it, and refuse to be identified with it. Social media has weaponized the label "transphobe" for anyone who objects to the narrative, and some of Shrier's Amazon reviewers parrot this. But this situation has alienated many progressives from their peers. One reviewer wrote, "Being a teenager should not be considered a medical condition."

No one is more protective than a mother bear. Shrier's book has stories about liberal families who were originally permissive about their daughter's peculiarities. But when mom realized what was happening, they left progressive states and successfully protected her offspring's normal development.

No one has been prosecuted for child abuse—yet.

A few other stories and sources

Another group who label themselves "non-binary" desire ambiguous genitals--and are willing to have an operation so they can have both a penis and a vagina. They call this "bottom" surgery. See Trans People Are Seeking Nonbinary Bottom Surgeries, an article found HERE. A related report describes a procedure called, "radial forearm phalloplasty with urethral lengthening, glansplasty, and no scrotoplasty... the first-ever bigenital/nonbinary confirmation surgery." This was from 2015, and the patient had complications.

Some physicians are speaking out against these trends. For example, Michael Egnor, MD, an ethics professor at Stonybrook Medical School, says that TGs are "An extraordinary medical atrocity."

The Connection Between The LGBTQ Movement, The World Economic Forum & Agenda 2030, link HERE.

The following is Sherman's comment on this report from Seattle: High School Cross-Country Runner Goes From 72nd to First Place; What's Her Secret?

A high school cross-country runner who placed 72nd as a boy last year won 1st place this year as a trans-girl. See the photo of the award ceremony with the boy (transitioned girl) at the top of the girls' award platform. One comment was, "The girls standing there, perfectly trained, afraid to speak what is true, is the mark of actual so-called 'privilege' in this country." It dawned on me then that one of the central purposes of the trans movement is to have the individual bow to the collective, no matter how wrong-headed the collective may be. To accept any insane narrative as valid.

Chapter 36
Dr. Miriam Grossman Exposes the Origins of the TG Disaster

On this guest podcast, Tim and May Hindmarsh at BSFreeMD.com interview Miriam Grossman, MD. She is a child psychiatrist and expert on the transgender phenomenon. Her book is, *You're Teaching My Child What?: A Physician Exposes the Lies of Sex Ed and How They Harm Your Child* (2009). She says that TG trends have been going on longer than is commonly recognized.

These ideas originated primarily from Dr. John Money, a pedophile psychologist. He believed that gender was learned rather than innate and was one of the first to claim that sexuality was a spectrum.

In 1966, he consulted on the case of two-year-old David Reimer, who had his penis accidentally burned off in a circumcision accident. Money recommended castration, estrogen supplementation, and raising the boy as a girl. During years of "therapy," he required that David and his brother Brian engage in nude simulated sex sessions complete with photography.

Robert Yoho, MD (ret)

SUBSTACK LINK

Between nine and eleven years old, David realized he was a boy. He switched back to living as a male when he was 14. He eventually went public about his life (Wikipedia):

[David Reimer's] case came to international attention in 1997 when he told his story to Milton Diamond, an academic sexologist who persuaded Reimer to allow him to report the outcome in order to dissuade physicians from treating other infants similarly. Soon after, Reimer went public with his story, and John Colapinto published a widely disseminated and influential account in Rolling Stone magazine in December 1997. The article won the National Magazine Award for Reporting.

This was later expanded into The New York Times best-selling biography As Nature Made Him: The Boy Who Was Raised as a Girl (2000), in which Colapinto described how—contrary to Money's reports—when living as Brenda, Reimer did not identify as a girl. He was ostracized and bullied by peers (who dubbed him "cavewoman"), and neither frilly dresses nor female hormones made him feel female.

David killed himself with a shotgun when he was 38. His brother Brian had died from an antidepressant overdose two years earlier.

Despite this, Mooney claimed, throughout his entire long and influential career, that the Reimer "reassignment" was successful. He asserted this was evidence that gender identity was learned rather than innate. These ideas were carried into the mainstream and spread like a disease.

The following is from Dr. Grossman's website:

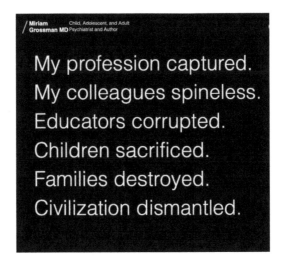

In her brilliant article, Jennifer Bilek reports that the LGBTQ+ network drives the transgender agenda. They are working closely with the techno-medical complex, big banks, international law firms, pharma giants, and corporate power to claim that we have multiple sexes.

The Pritzkers below have Hyatt Hotel money, and wealthy people do whatever they want. This includes eviscerating our values, culture, and rationality.

Robert Yoho, MD (ret)

Philanthropist Jennifer (formerly James) Pritzker
(Wikipedia Commons)

[This family's] investments [promote transgender] surgeries and drugs, and by instituting rapid language
reforms to prop up these new identities and induce institutions and individuals to normalize them. In 2018, for
example, at the Ronald Reagan Medical Center at the
University of California Los Angeles (where the
Pritzkers are major donors and hold various titles), the
Department of Obstetrics and Gynecology advertised
several options for young females who think they can be
men to have their reproductive organs removed, a proce-
dure termed "gender-affirming care."

Other sources
Toby Rogers writes that big Pharma is promoting the
TS agenda: "Trans messaging is too sophisticated to be the
work of a small sexual minority dealing with severe health
issues."

HERE is another of Dr. Grossman's interviews.

Cassandra's Memo

Quentin Van Meter, M.D., FCP, has journal articles and academic YouTube lectures analyzing the TG phenomenon, including THIS one, The Terrible Fraud of 'Transgender Medicine.' Longer-term studies show early death for TGs due to hormone imbalances.

More information than you can stand to read about Money is in this article: John Money, the Charlatan Godfather of the Transgender Movement.

Chapter 37
A Transgender Surgeon's Point of View

My Seattle colleague Tony Mangubat, MD, tells his story about how he became a cosmetic surgeon for the worldwide TG community. Half of what he does now is "top" surgery, which is breast removal for a genetic female who wants to transition to a male. He also describes other types of masculinizing procedures he performs. As you will hear, Tony is sympathetic and respectful toward his patients.

The woke crowd concocted new pronouns for TGs who think they are male, female, or somewhere in between. Those of us who rely on our original equipment for guidance have been generously provided with others. It gets confusing, but Tony schools me about it. If you want to be sure you do not offend your diversity-inclined colleagues, listen to the podcast twice.

SUBSTACK LINK The video is HERE on Rumble.

Cassandra's Memo

Dr. Mangubat's TickTock channel is TicDocTony, his website is HERE. and "Top surgeon" links are HERE and HERE. There are testimonial videos and before/after photos.

Disclosure: Tony is an old friend (I am the young friend, ha). I do not inject opinions of my own into his interview.

There is a meme floating around that explains the pronouns perfectly. It has three photos of a gradually disappearing girl. The caption is, "Although I was born visible, I now identify as invisible. I am trans-parent. My pronouns are who/where." If you understand this, you pass the pronoun test.

Chapter 38
Diversion: Do Not Cut the Rope on Australia

I f you tour World War II memorials in France, you might conclude that the Resistance threw the Germans out of France by themselves. But we all know—or at least everyone but the French knows—that the Allies saved them.

Wikipedia tells the truth for once: "The French Resistance was a collection of organizations that fought the Nazi occupation of France and the collaborationist Vichy regime during the Second World War. Resistance cells were small groups of armed men and women who, in addition to their guerrilla warfare activities, were also publishers of underground newspapers, providers of first-hand intelligence information, and maintainers of escape networks that helped Allied soldiers and airmen trapped behind enemy lines."

An obviously staged photo of an American officer
protected by a French partisan during World War II
(Wikipedia).

* * *

My friend Sandy from Australia and her country are in the
middle of a monstrous mugging-murder. She and her
"mates" (as they say "down under") are typically good-
natured, somewhat innocent people who resemble our
lovely Canadians. They are not up to the task of defending
themselves against the global psychopaths. The British and
Americans are far tougher, but I also have doubts about us.

Here is an email from Sandy:

Hi Robert

*I thought I would send this update, as you asked how it's
going over here. I know we have to take some legal action,
but all such efforts in the past have failed because they delay,
postpone, and call in false 'experts' who are not really experts.*

The whole thing is rigged. Nevertheless, I am praying for a miracle from this process. You guys in the USA have a much better judicial system (even with the flaws) compared to Australia. Almost all our doors are closed in this prison camp. I love what RFK, Jr, has been able to do... and the legal team with Del Bigtree.

The criminal syndicate will shut down the economy, kill small businesses, and make everyone beholden to the government and forced to take their handouts with strings attached - just like the mafia. The coup d'etat of the totalitarian state. These sociopaths and their agenda are the biggest threat to humanity ever. We face annihilation if they are not brought to justice... If it's not the poison in the jabs, it will be people killing each other to get food. That's insane on steroids.

Yes, there is an awakening, but we need the awakening to happen also in the top rungs of power so that justice can be ENFORCED legally. There is so much proof of the skullduggery of those in power (see RFK, Jr's book The Real Anthony Fauci*). Why are these people not arrested and prosecuted for their crimes? You can't expect the citizenry to arrest these mafiosos unless you want a civil war and lots of bloodshed... That's clearly not the way to go, but it seems to be how they are trying to ignite the powder keg.*

Where are the Navy Seals and elite soldiers when you need them?

Anyway, we do what we can in our small circle of influence to help people buckle up and prepare for a bumpy ride before it gets better again.

Take care, and cheers,
Sandy

. . .

Cassandra's Memo

Here is an account of a mountaineering accident relevant to our situation with Sandy. Two climbers were in a remote, dangerous place with no way to communicate with the outside world or chance of rescue. One of them fell.

> He told me very calmly that he had broken his leg. He looked pathetic, and my immediate thought came without any emotion, You're f****d, matey. You're dead... no two ways about it! I think he knew it too. I could see it in his face. It was all totally rational. I knew where we were, I took in everything around me instantly, and knew he was dead. It never occurred to me that I might also die. I accepted without question that I could get off the mountain alone. I had no doubt about that.
>
> — From Joe Simpson's classic *Touching the Void* (1988).

With a herculean effort, Joe's partner Simon was able to get the injured man most of the way down the mountain. But near the bottom, after risking his life in the rescue attempt, he decided to cut the rope holding his partner in half. Joe dropped 100 feet into a crevasse at the base of the mountain. Simon left him for dead and rescued himself with the remaining part of their rope. I will not spoil the rest of the story except that the injured climber survived to write the book.

A friend of mine met these people at a climbing area years later. He told me they were screaming at each other and were taking ridiculous risks. He thought they were both insane.

SUBSTACK LINK

279

Can we do anything for Sandy?

Sadly, we are in deep s***t ourselves, and I have few answers. Cutting the rope on anyone seems like a terrible option, but we must somehow set our own house in order before we can save anyone else. It is a brutal situation.

The following is Sandy's latest email. I asked her if the injections were being forced on anyone in Australia. She said laws mandating physical force were on the books, but:

There are no places where they hold you down and jab. But certainly intimidation and coercion via jobs in medical professions, teachers, airlines etc. People are leaving these professions. You can't get good service anymore. It's chaotic as too many young inexperienced people or migrants are left to do their thing... Often without enough training and supervision. But many are waking up now to the scam of it...

I pray we can somehow carry the day to help them.

Part Nine

Climatology is Even More Bogus Than Medicine

Chapter 39
Dr. Patrick Moore, Founder of Greenpeace, Explains Climate Frauds

The environmental movement was hijacked by political and social activists who learned to use green language to cloak agendas that had more to do with anticapitalism and antiglobalization than with science or ecology.

— Patrick Moore

We all want to be good stewards of the Earth. No one, least of all Dr. Moore, advocates polluting our world or wasting resources. But nearly everything commonly promoted about environmental issues is wrong.

We have been told "all the scientists" believe the end is nigh. Some young people have been so badly damaged by the horror tales that they refuse to have children. But "climate change" is a pseudo-religion rather than reality, and the predicted worldwide catastrophes are fables rather than science. Once you understand what is known, you will have far less to worry about.

SUBSTACK LINK for Dr. Moore's interview. Bitchute version HERE.

Dr. Moore describes in clear, simple words why global warming and carbon theories are wrong. He also debunks other myths:

- The increase in forest fires is due to mismanagement, not increasing temperatures.
- The Texas-sized island of plastic floating in the Pacific Ocean does not exist.
- Polar bears are not going extinct—they are multiplying so well that they threaten the Inuit Indians.

These and many other stories are inflicted on us to inflame, irritate, and harvest more money for fraudulent "climate research." Moore's critics call him a "climate denier." This is Orwellian doublespeak—a phrase designed to squash questions and bully anyone with common sense. Here is the truth:

•31,000 US scientists and professionals signed a document repudiating the CO_2 theory of climate change. References and much more are HERE and HERE.

Cassandra's Memo

- The Arctic ice has been shrinking since the early 1990s. However, the Antarctic icecap has recorded the highest ice levels ever. This more than offsets the shrinkage in the north.
- We have 300,000 years of accurate atmospheric CO_2 and temperature data from sources such as polar ice cap drilling. Other data extends covers hundreds of millions of years. CO_2 typically *follows* rather than *predicts* temperatures, which means there is no cause and effect. The Milankovitch Cycle, a far more significant phenomenon, creates cooling and major glaciations every 100,000 years. This is related to the change in the globe's tilt on its axis.
- Current CO_2 levels are not far above the low levels that nearly extinguished life 300 million years ago. And since mammals flourished on Earth when the CO_2 level was five times today's, we can stop worrying about the tiny increase.

The universal misconception about climatology is that our personal time frame and perceptions are relevant. While "I have seen it with my own eyes" may be the best measure for most human observations, it is meaningless for this field. Since we have data about trends occurring over hundreds of millions of years, we are sure that nothing worrisome is happening now.

* * *

Background: Moore received his Ph.D. in ecology in the mid-1960s and started as a radical environmental activist. As co-founder of Greenpeace, he played a critical role in stopping hydrogen bomb testing in Alaska. He was arrested trying to save baby seals. To protect whales, he put himself in front of the harpoons of Soviet factory ships. Worldwide, whale populations continue to recover because of work like this.

Greenpeace's original mission was to save humanity from nuclear war. Dr. Moore explains how they confused nuclear weaponry with safe, beneficial, and potentially cheap atomic power. When Greenpeace became violent and started sensationalizing, he decided they were chasing funding rather than saving the world and quit the group.

Moore does not mention what Alex Epstein (next chapter) says openly—that these climate frauds are being used to intimidate and impoverish the world's people. This is starvation for developing countries.

* * *

Resources: Moore's 20-minute video HERE totally debunks the carbon and global warming "science" that is being fed to us. I copied the slides and explanations from his talk HERE and HERE. (For print readers, these links are at the QR codes below). If you spend 15 minutes scanning these, you will never worry about these issues again.

Moore's 2022 book, *Fake Invisible Catastrophes and Threats of Doom*, is on Amazon HERE. His earlier book is *Confessions of a Greenpeace Dropout* (2010). Both are well-written, easy reads, and they have thousands of five-star Amazon reviews.

HERE is another Patrick Moore podcast.

HERE is an excellent video by an economist: The False Promise of Green Energy (Prof. Andrew Morriss - Acton Institute).

PSYOP-CLIMATE-CHANGE: Top Climate Scientist Slams "Goebellian" Climate Alarm and "Ridiculous" Attempts to Demonise "Fertiliser" Carbon Dioxide.

PSYOP-CLIMATE-CHANGE: The Absurd CO_2 Scam

PSYOP-CLIMATE-CHANGE Exposed: CO_2 in Air Increased in 2 Centuries by 1 Molecule in 10,000

PSYOP-CLIMATE-CHANGE Update: 1,107 Scientists & Professionals From Across The World Led By The Norwegian Physics Nobel Prize Laureate Professor Ivar Giaever Declare: "There Is No Climate Emergency"

SUBSTACK LINK

SUBSTACK LINK

Robert Yoho, MD (ret)

Chapter 40
"Climate Denier" Alex Epstein

[The] extremely positive plant effects of CO_2 are scientifically uncontroversial yet practically never mentioned, even by the climate-science community. This is a dereliction of duty. It is our responsibility to look at the big picture, all positives and negatives, without prejudice. If they think the plant positives are outweighed, they can give their reasons. But to ignore the fertilizer effect and to fail to include it when discussing the impacts of CO_2 is dishonest...

My reading of the evidence is that there is a mild greenhouse effect in the direction human beings have always wanted—warmer—and a significant fertilizer effect in the direction human beings have always wanted —more plant life. I believe that the public discussion is prejudiced by an assumption that human impacts are bad, which causes us to fear and disapprove of the idea of affecting climate...

— Alex J. Epstein

I n his bestseller, *The Moral Case for Fossil Fuels,* Alex Epstein says that the mainstream "ecology" story is a lie. His book is well-written, readable, and has 1117 Amazon reviews averaging 4.8/5.

Eighty-seven percent of all human energy is derived from coal, oil, and natural gas. But for over 30 years, the "experts" and media have predicted that these practices would either incinerate us or drown us as sea levels rose. Their Biblical-scale disaster of resource depletion, pollution, and climate degeneration never happened. Instead, as billions of people obtained access to cheap, reliable energy, the environment and the quality of human life both improved.

Although fossil fuel use increased by 80 percent between 1980 and 2012, Epstein shows that we are unlikely to run out of Earth's plentiful coal, oil, and natural gas energy for thousands of years. He says, "The amount of raw matter and energy on this planet is so incomprehensibly vast that it is nonsensical to speculate about running out of it."

Fear-mongering about global cooling preceded the current fad of global warming. And although sea levels rose dramatically 10,000 years ago, they are stable today.

Solar and wind energy function poorly for several reasons. These source inputs are episodic and unreliable, so expensive storage batteries are required. The only support for claims that this "green" energy is economically viable are calculations made during brief, ideal conditions, as was recently done for Germany. Constructing the equipment requires expensive fossil fuels, but this was not included. Solar and wind power are costly, unscalable, unreliable, and a net waste of energy.

Third-world countries living on the edge of poverty— and ultimately starvation—cannot afford to toy with these ideas. They need conventional, reliable energy sources to survive.

"Biomass" fuels such as alcohol from corn can poten- tially scale and produce more energy than solar or wind. However, they are expensive and making them drives food prices up.

Epstein notes that nuclear energy is hated by "environ- mentalists," who equate it with the hazards of hydrogen bombs. But modern power plants cannot explode, and commercial production of atomic energy in the free world has not led to a single death. The radioactivity released is insignificant, and the waste is now easily managed.

Government regulation cripples US nuclear power. The industry is scalable, and it is cheap without this burden. Small reactors could be brought on line in just a few years.

Nuclear power plants produce so much energy—they operate 90 percent of the time—that they pay back their construction costs *in their first six (6) weeks up and running*. HERE is a podcast by "Doomberg" on the What Bitcoin Did podcast by Peter McCormack that explains this. He also describes the political environment that hobbles nuclear energy worldwide and gives a comprehensive summary of other energy sources.

SUBSTACK LINK

Hydroelectric is cheap and clean, but activists hate it, too, because they see it as altering Mother Earth. Coal is the most plentiful fossil fuel, and recent advances have made burning it far cleaner.

The world population doubled in my lifetime. But we are far better fed than ever because of the plentiful fossil fuel used in farming. Agricultural advances have improved crop yields as well.

Atmospheric CO_2 has a greening or fertilizing effect on plant life, which makes the Earth more livable. Denial of this allows the claim, "When you use fossil fuels, you have to consider all the environmental costs." This is wrong—

there are net environmental *advantages* to more CO_2 production and release.

The warming or greenhouse effect of CO_2 is modest, if it exists at all. Epstein credits the possibility that it might have a small impact, but other authors think CO_2 effects approach zero. Compared to water vapor, a vastly more common substance, CO_2 is inconsequential. Climate predictions are notoriously unreliable because there are so many variables. Epstein says, "Every climate model based on CO_2 as a major climate driver has been a failure."

Worldwide temperatures have risen about .8 degree Celsius in the past 150 years and not at all since 1998. But great rewards await those who get media attention, and the easiest way to do it is by proclaiming doom.

Objections to fracking based on flammable gas ejected from drinking water are sensationalized lies. The often-filmed show of lighting tap water on fire involves superficial groundwater gases such as methane. Fracking occurs many thousands of feet deep.

Obama claimed on Twitter, "Ninety-seven percent of scientists agree, # climate change is real, man-made, and dangerous." But there is no agreement about any of these ridiculous claims, which were concocted by "climate scientists" seeking funding. The 97 percent figure came from a woke website promoting climate apocalypse. Epstein wrote, "Think about how many times you hear that 97 percent or some similar figure thrown around. It's based on crude manipulation propagated by people whose ideological agenda it serves. It is a license to intimidate."

The people advancing this agenda are disdainful of human life. They seem to believe that all of our impacts are wrong and fantasize about a planet with far fewer or even no people.

The actual problem today is that, despite all the advances, we still have billions starving and dying because they lack enough energy to feed themselves. Epstein says we must apologize to the fossil fuel industry because increased fossil fuel usage correlates with increased lifespan, income, and other positive effects.

Sources

Epstein's latest book is *Fossil Future: Why Global Human Flourishing Requires More Oil, Coal, and Natural Gas, Not Less* (2022). It has nearly 1000 reviews averaging 4.7 stars. He describes how fossil fuels have cleaned up the environment and improved human flourishing. His Substack blog is AlexEpstein.substack.com.

William Briggs, a climate expert without outside funding, wrote, "The same foundational problems in 'climate change,' and the burning need to protect these problems from scrutiny, are found in every branch of science."

The Man Who Invented Climate Change HERE is about how climate change frauds are being used to advance the "Reset" and effect wealth transfer.

Contributor comment: *If you are outside and your hair is wet, you do not have to be a meteorologist to know it is raining. Ignore experts, look at the evidence, and decide for yourself.*

Chapter 41
Oil is Safe, Clean, and Prevents Starvation

Efforts to cease using crude oil are the greatest threat to civilization's eight billion people.

— Ronald Stein

We have too little CO_2, not too much.
CO_2 is the gas of life.
CO_2 induces plant life.
CO_2 is not a control knob for climate; no legitimate research can demonstrate that CO_2 impacts global temperatures in any way.

PSYOP-CLIMATE-CHANGE is nothing more than the depopulation of carbon-based lifeforms.

We currently have far too little CO_2, as per this vital chart:

600 million years of CO2 data reveals current CO$_2$ starvation

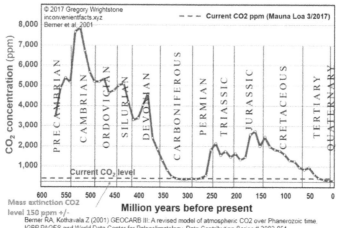

At around 150 ppm (parts per million) of CO2, life on Earth essentially dies. But as the CO2 increases, it's almost as if the planetary terraforming operation is accelerating in plain sight.

Yoho explanation of the graph. *This is the history of atmospheric CO2 levels. Mammals thrived through CO2 levels of 2700 ppm during the Jurassic Era, 175 million years ago. Over the last 150 million years, the level dramatically declined. It is now 421 ppm, not far above where all life starts to die—175 ppm. The industrial revolution may have rescued life on Earth, because it slightly increased CO2.*

If the "green" agenda were not a depopulation and control scheme, then they would primarily be concerned with planetary pollution. But just as the vaccine campaigns in African nations were eugenics programs that murdered and maimed so many, the developing world is experiencing increasing famines and population reductions from this

One World Government "green" world order program, and it will become far worse over the coming weeks and months, culminating in mass population reductions. Or what Black Lives Matter in Africa really looks like. Thankfully, African American vaccine "hesitancy" is extremely high.

"Climate change" is nothing more than the penultimate Technocratic power grab to usher in the 4th Industrial Revolution via the Great Posthuman Reset. It is a total reality inversion just as PSYOP-19 was and continues to be en route to PSYOP-22 and all of the other bio-fascist scams that will be increasingly blamed on "climate change."

SUBSTACK LINK

Blaming the gas of life (and carbon-based lifeforms) for all things "climate change" is truly the ultimate sleight of hand. There is to date not a single legitimate research study that definitively proves CO_2 has a single negative impact on anything whatsoever. Every research study to date is fear-mongering speculation and nothing more. The scientific "consensus" that is often cited by brainwashed Death Cultists is a public relations propaganda campaign run by the MSM that always excludes the greater consensus of the more qualified scientists that have all called b.s. on this scam.

This "climate change" operation that went from the fear of an ice age in the 1970s to anthropogenic global warming (AGW) to today's exceedingly vague label dates back to the Club of Rome, a shadowy "nonprofit" funded by the Technocratic cabal that has been since the 1960s slowly and methodically seeding this murderous program.

And now that we have officially entered the Grand Solar Minimum that will drive global temperatures down, the narrative will be forced to shift to blaming humans and their CO_2 on the cold — or why it is best to hurry up and execute this whole takeover program before having to once again alter the narrative:

We are running out of time and urgent action is needed. These challenges are global, and we must meet them with a global response that drives action on the ground.

The only thing the Cult and its useful idiot puppets are running out of pertains to their sociopathic power grab scams. They are in a hurry because they have been found out by a large enough percentage of the global population.

China is anti-"Green" World Order, not even bothering to install inexpensive cleaning scrubbers on their coal plant stacks that eliminate nearly all pollution. But they constantly lie about their intentions.

Life without oil is not as simple a you may think. Renewable energy is intermittent electricity from either breezes or sunshine. Climate change might possibly impact humanity, but a mandate to live without the products manufactured from oil will mandate lifestyles of the 1800s, the horse and buggy days. This is the greatest threat in our lifetimes to civilization's eight billion residents.

World leaders make no mention that the entire pharmaceutical industry, chemical industry, materials science, energy, transportation, heating, etc. are dependent on the same fossil fuels that they want to rid the world of. Attempting to attain a decarbonized world like the one that existed in the 1800s and before could result in billions of fatalities from disease, malnutrition, and weather-related deaths. In contrast, changes in climate are projected (and who trusts predictions of the future) in millions of fatalities.

Surprisingly, the fossil fuels infrastructure are less invasive than the mining for exotic minerals and metals in developing countries to support solar and wind energy. This is destroying the planet through environmental degradation and human atrocities inflicted upon people with yellow, brown, and black skin. The 2022 Pulitzer Prize-nominated book *Clean Energy Exploitations – Helping Citizens Understand the Environmental and Humanity Abuses That Support Clean Energy* does an excellent job of discussing the lack of transparency in the world of the green movement's impact on humanity.

Of the three fossil fuels of coal, natural gas, and crude oil, crude oil is the only one primarily used to manufacture products that are the basis of the economy.

Crude oil is virtually useless unless it is refined into its derivatives. These are the basis of more than 6,000 important products that did not exist before the 1900s. They are also the fuels that move the heavy-weight and long-range requirements of more than 50,000 jets, more than 50,000 merchant ships, and the military and space program.

The liquid fuels and products produced from this hydrocarbon processing aided the advancement of rocket technology, leading humans to break the boundaries of space and place satellites into geosynchronous orbit. These advances significantly evolved the way the world communicates, navigates, and explores not only Earth but the distant cosmos.

All the products needed to make the parts for vehicles, wind turbines, solar panels, planes, ships, medical supplies, tires, asphalt, and fertilizer are made with the oil derivatives manufactured from crude oil. Wind turbines and solar panels are able to generate intermittent electricity, but they cannot manufacture anything.

Everything that needs electricity, from lights, vehicles, iPhones, defibrillators, computers, telecommunications, etc., are all made with the oil derivatives manufactured from crude oil. There would be nothing to power in a world without fossil fuels.

About the Author: Ronald Stein is the Founder and Ambassador for Energy & Infrastructure of PTS Advance, headquartered in Irvine, California. To read the original post, see HERE.

Chapter 42
Diversion: Magic Sunglasses Shatter the Glogal Warming Hoax

The low levels of the Colorado River are being promoted as yet another end-times event. But in the context of even the past 250 years, today's decreased rainfall in our West is routine (ref: Patrick Moore).

The Anasazi Indian civilization near here lasted more than 1000 years but likely died due to drought between 1090 and 1130 AD. We should not fear that because adequately deployed nuclear energy would inexpensively harvest purified water from the oceans. But since we are over-regulated, we have built no new nuclear power plants in the US since the 1970s. Supply and demand should cure these problems eventually.

All my other sunglasses are from the Dollar General store. These
retail for $300 and were a gift. Photo credit: DP

Note: This part of the River is backed up behind a dam,
which promotes evaporative loss.

Part Ten

I Wish I Had Never Heard of the Reset Prime Movers

Chapter 43
The Bankers Eat Their Lunch and Yours as Well

If you have not thrown up your breakfast by 11 am on any given day, you are not paying attention.

— Paraphrased from a saying by Sherman

By Christian Elliot, December 29, 2021, source HERE, abridged and read by Yoho. Podcast at this LINK.

International bankers want to get rid of cash and use controlled cryptocurrency to monitor everyone, everywhere. Agustin Carstens, the general manager of the Bank for International Settlements famously explains this in a one minute video HERE (required).

The Federal Reserve Bank and the Bank for International Settlements are the planet's moneylenders. They operate in secret and are only accountable to their private shareholders. The International Monetary Fund wields vast powers as well.

A few thousand people manage and control these

groups. They openly document their plans on websites, at conferences, and even with patent filings. They maintain control by compromising and blackmailing their subordinates and others.

Since World War I, the entire global economy became progressively more dominated by these privately owned central banks. As they loaned money to governments, and more "national debt" was owed, the banks acquired more control.

SUBSTACK LINK 1

SUBSTACK LINK 2

The Federal Reserve Bank (the Fed) was created in 1914. It was a new privately-owned national bank. It:

- Turned us away from individual state banking systems. Only North Dakota now remains.
- Controlled the nation's currency.
- Set up a private bank from which the government borrows.
- Broke the "gold standard," the requirement that something tangible backs money.
- Before this, paper money could be freely exchanged for gold stored in a vault. After this, the Fed was allowed to print "fiat" dollars, which means inking paper and calling it valuable. After this, politicians did not need to raise taxes when they made a campaign promise or fought a war. After this, they could agree to raise the "debt ceiling" instead of working with a fixed money supply as individuals do. And so they have proceeded to do this more than 70 times since the 1960s. It is like raising a personal credit card limit when you run out of money.

Our federal central-banking system:

- Benefits those with the closest relationships to the money printer.
- Allows the government to create more money whenever there is a perceived crisis.
- Allows unchecked spending.
- Creates inflation.
- Devalues the currency.
- Permits more and more government borrowing, which drives inflation higher.

From 1862 to 1994, the US currency had a banner that read "United States Note," It now reads "Federal Reserve Note."

We have become hooked on the myth that government spending benefits us. The short-term windfall seems reasonable for a while. But the result is that central banking steals from the poor and gives to the rich.

Our monetary system is being engineered to create a situation where few, except the wealthy, have substantial personal property. The bankers call it the "Great Reset." The famous "you will own nothing and be happy" Facebook video is from the World Economic Forum website. It describes what they want the world to look like by 2030. Access it HERE, and read more HERE.

The US Federal Reserve is only accountable to the bank's private owners. They keep their assets and decision process secret and have never been publicly audited. The Rothschild family holds majority ownership, and several international banks hold minority shares.

Mayer Amschel Rothschild once said, "Give me control of the economics of a country, and I care not who makes her laws. The few who understand the system will either be so interested in its profits or so dependent on its favors, that there will be no opposition from that class." Credit-card companies keep people enslaved using interest that never ends, and private central banks keep nations enslaved with the same method. Elected leaders are endlessly beholden to the wishes of the financiers because of debt.

Montagu Norman, governor of the Bank of England in the early 20th century, believed that he and his confederates literally owned their creditors:

Cassandra's Memo

Capital must protect itself in every possible way, both by combination and legislation. Debts must be collected, mortgages foreclosed as rapidly as possible. When, through the process of law, the common people lose their homes, they will become docile and more easily governed through the strong arm of the government applied through the central power of wealth under leading financiers. These truths are well known among our principal men, who are now engaged in forming an imperialism to govern the world. By dividing the voters through the political party system, we can get them to expend their energies in fighting for questions of no importance. It is thus, by discrete action, we can ensure for ourselves that which has been so well planned and so successfully accomplished.

— from a 1924 address to the US Bankers' Association

Norman's modern successors share these attitudes.

Rulers invariably run out of money because they cannot raise taxes indefinitely. They then borrow the funds from wealthy families using central banks. These institutions collect interest and demand favors. This system allows the rich to exert irresistible influence over governments.

The Bank for International Settlements (BIS) is the organization of central banks that manages the world's money supply. Its members are private banks owned by wealthy families from at least 60 countries. It is located in Basel, Switzerland, and was founded in 1930. It:

- Meets in secrecy
- Does not take minutes

- Cannot be audited
- Does not pay taxes
- Cannot be sued
- Has its own police force
- Even has its own flag
- Operates independently of any government.

The group's sole loyalty is to its capital, which "must protect itself at all costs." Centralized power and control are the owners' goals.

After WWII, the "leading financiers" created the International Monetary Fund (IMF). This institution coordinates the money flow between central banks and decides the global exchange rates. This allows them to control which national currencies retain their value and which do not. Since the IMF can potentially crush any economy, they exert at least as much control over countries as their national leaders.

The Fed, the BIS, and the IMF rule the global money supply. These are under the command of a few ultra-wealthy people.

Cassandra's Memo

The Bank of International Settlements is shaped like a giant boot.

If you want a picture of the future, imagine a boot stamping on a human face—forever.

— George Orwell, *1984*

Dwight D. Eisenhower, in his 1961 farewell speech as President of the United States, warned of the dangers of military and scientific power in combination:

We face a hostile ideology, global in scope, atheistic in character, ruthless in purpose, and insidious in method. We must guard against the acquisition of unwarranted influence, whether sought or unsought, by the military-industrial complex.

The potential for the disastrous rise of misplaced power exists and will persist. We must never let the weight of this combination endanger our liberties or democratic processes. We must also be alert to the...

danger that public policy could itself become the captive of a scientific-technological elite.

His successor, John F. Kennedy, said something similar:

We are opposed around the world by a monolithic and ruthless conspiracy that relies primarily on covert means for expanding its sphere of influence—on infiltration instead of invasion, on subversion instead of elections, on intimidation instead of free choice, on guerrillas by night instead of armies by day. It is a system that has conscripted vast human and material resources into the building of tightly-knit, highly efficient machines that combine military, diplomatic, intelligence, economic, scientific, and political operations.

Kennedy was taking steps to correct the situation. The following is from Stephen Mitford Goodson's *A History of Central Banking and the Enslavement of Mankind*:

On June 4th, 1963, President John F. Kennedy issued Executive Order No. 11110, which instructed the Treasury to print $4 billion worth of $2 and $5 bills. These bills, backed by silver in the Treasury's vaults, were issued free of debt and interest, with the seigniorage accruing not to the privately-owned US Federal Reserve Bank but to the US government. This note issue formed part of Kennedy's long-term plan to reduce the power of the US Federal Reserve Bank. On November 22, 1963, Kennedy was shot down by assassin(s) in Dallas, Texas.

Economist David Stockman commented on Alan Greenspan's part in this story:

Before Alan Greenspan fell off the wagon in pursuit of government power, position, praise, and riches, in his 1966 speech, "Gold and Economic Freedom," he said the following: "In the absence of the gold standard, there is no way to protect savings from confiscation through inflation...The financial policy of the welfare state requires that there be no way for the owners of wealth to protect themselves. Deficit spending is simply a scheme for the confiscation of wealth."

Alan Greenspan took the helm of the Fed in 1987. Some said he sold his soul to the devil and America to the central bank. If people like him prevail, we will soon live in a real-life version of the novel 1984.

Where we are today. THIS video by Tim Gielen explains how the global financial system has been consolidated and how the media is controlled (required). These forces have come together and are attempting to create a criminal, dystopian "New World Order."

Blackrock. Founded in 1988, this is one of the world's two most powerful financial asset management companies. THIS two-minute video explains how Black-Rock and the Fed secretly collaborate. They see themselves as Montagu Norman's "principal men... engage[d] in forming an imperialism to govern the world." HERE is a 29-second video of Larry Fink, the founder of Black Rock. He claims the global economy prefers totalitarianism because democracies are "messy."

The threat of central bank digital currencies. Biden's nominee for one of the top banking regulator positions was Saule Omarova. From *Epoch Times* November 9, 2021:

It would be best, she outlined in a series of articles and papers, to virtually abolish private banking. Every American would have a bank account set up at the Fed, and authorities would be free to inflate the currency by issuing interest on the deposits or even crediting the accounts directly. To counter inflation, the Fed could also slash interest rates or even, if all else fails, take away people's money as needed, she proposed in a recent paper.

Omarova says that people spending their money (cash) without government tracking is wrong. Thankfully, Omarova's nomination was withdrawn, but who will come next?

Understanding the system. Ronald Bernard is a former Dutch banker who worked his way into the inner circle of the people who pulled the central banking strings. HERE is his chilling testimony about them from 2018, and HERE is more. It is a window into bankers' psychology.

Catherine Austin Fitts, the publisher of The Solari Report, describes today's reality:

> Just like there is a magical place called Disney World where an underground infrastructure creates the experiences we see above ground, so too is there an invisible, underground economy that dictates what happens in the "above ground" economy that the rest of us 99% interact within.

Austin-Fitts says that what is different today is that those in control have become so powerful that they are cutting the political leaders out.

The global debt load is unsustainable, the fiat system will collapse, and the central bankers know it. They are out of moves and are manufacturing "The Great Reset" crisis so they can present themselves as saviors. The globalists have told us about their ideas for the future. "Event 201" was a multi-national event funded by Dustin Moskovitz, the co-founder of Facebook, that simulated a global Coronavirus pandemic response. Following the script, the pandemic was instigated a few months later.

Their public simulations include:

- A 10-nations summit to simulate a "cyberattack" on the global financial system
- The food-industry meltdown simulation seen through the lens of "climate change"
- A patent (WO2020060606A1) was granted in 2018 for "Cryptocurrency system using body activity data." This is an ominous document about governmental behavior control.
- Prince Charles called for trillions of dollars and a "warlike" effort to combat the emerging "climate crisis." More money printing and inflation are part of these plans. Katherine Austin Fitz comments further about the situation HERE.

How to stop it, short term: Dismantle the Covid frauds

Our founders designed the US democracy with checks and balances between the three government branches. Our executive and legislative branches are heavily compromised, and the courts are still partially functioning. They are rejecting some of the mandates and other parts of this agenda. The result is that many big businesses are dropping injection mandates.

Longer term: Fight central banking

• Use cash. The last thing the globalists want is for us to be able to transact outside their control grid. All of us using cash just one day a week would go a long way.

• Find a local bank not part of the "tapeworm 20" (HERE) that invests our money in the globalist consolidation of wealth. To find a good bank, read THIS.

• Start spending and investing your money strategically. Shift your money away from corporations that are participating in the criminal conspiracy.

• See the chapter about Bitcoin in part 11. It is the only cryptocurrency worth considering and the only legitimate, decentralized threat to central banking. Bitcoin can give the world a stable currency with no person or group controlling the money supply. If Bill Gates and his billionaire buddies tell you not to invest in it, and China is banning it, it must have merit.

Counterpoint

The "global elites" have deeply ridiculous ideas and would be pathetic if they were less powerful. They praise the ideas of Karl Marx and the Bolsheviks and seem to worship today's China—all models that have been tested exhaustively and failed repeatedly. Their religion is "Transhumanism," which presents technology as the highest power. Here are some of their beliefs:

• Man will merge with machines in the "Singularity" to achieve superhuman life extension or
possibly immortality.

• Gadgets can cure ignorance, loneliness, sadness,

disease, old age, and death. We must become this new post-human combination with machines to survive.

• Robots will become conscious and possibly dominate us as Skynet does in the Terminator movies. (And I thought this was out of fashion.)

• Some have contracted to get their heads chopped off, then frozen after they die so they can be reawakened later. See the second source below.

Psychopaths who have cheated their way to untold worldly success have delusions that they can bribe or swindle their way out of death's inevitability. Since lies are in their DNA, accepting something this absurd is a small step for them. They are atheists, their fears are palpable, and we are witnessing their defense mechanisms.

Although *average* human survival has improved, extending our *maximum* lifespans remains a pipe dream. People with unrealistic wishes and an idiotic faith in technology get no special dispensation. As these men age and become obsessed with their mortality, they miss the consolation prize—impermanence makes life sweeter.

Sources

For this essay, I abridged and added to Christian Elliot's December 29, 2021 post HERE. For my podcast with him, see this LINK. He runs an organization that is helping people prepare.

Freezing People Is (Not) Easy: My Adventures In Cryonics (2014) describes how alcor.org will, for a fee, decapitate you and freeze your head. They have yet to awaken anyone.

I blew my lunch early when I read the essay HERE. Good luck keeping yours down.

A History of Central Banking and the Enslavement of Mankind by Stephen Mitford Goodson is a frequently censored must-read. Highly recommended.

Whitney Webb's two-volume *One Nation Under Blackmail* explains the history of these criminals in the 20th century. She started researching Jeffrey Epstein, and he led her to many others. Listen to her Mercola interview HERE.

The international network of tax and oversight-exempt institutions is summarized HERE on the Sharp Edge & Corey Lynn. The author presents some solutions. Warning: this is X rated.

HERE is an overview of the history of the depopulation agenda.

Chapter 44
Mercola: The Great Reset Plan and its Worldwide Criminal Network

I 've always felt that fascism is a more natural governmental condition than democracy. Democracy is a grace. It's something essentially splendid because it's not at all routine or automatic. Fascism goes back to our infancy and childhood, where we were always told how to live. We were told, Yes, you may do this; no, you may not do that. So the secret of fascism is that it has this appeal to people whose later lives are not satisfactory.

—Norman Mailer

Analysis by Dr. Joseph Mercola, February 17, 2022. Read by Robert Yoho. This confirms what you learned in the last chapter. It deserves a speed-read.

STORY AT-A-GLANCE

The German Club of Clear Words describes the network of individuals and organizations responsible for the COVID scam

The Bill & Melinda Gates Foundation

appears to be near the top, or the center, of this COVID plandemic network. Gates is also a major funder of mainstream media, and his network extends into global food and climate change policy

The Gates Foundation, through its funding of the World Economic Forum (WEF), also plays an important role in The Great Reset, which was officially unveiled during a WEF summit in May 2020

According to their plan, every aspect of life and society is scheduled to be "reset". That's where this criminal COVID enterprise is trying to take us

SUBSTACK LINK

The German Club Der Klaren Worte, or the Club of Clear Words, describes the network of individuals and organizations responsible for the COVID scam in a video. It is led by journalist and filmmaker Markus Langemann. He says that it's not necessarily the people with the best ideas who win in life. Rather, the winners are those in the "right"

network — a network with people in high places. Never underestimate the power of a network.

Some networks are visible. One example would be an alumni network that you can join and use to promote your career. Other networks are more hidden, secretive, and exclusive, and can only be entered into by an invitation from another member.

Whether visible or not, just about any network can be identified by connecting the dots between individuals and organizations. Who's working with whom, where, and why? Who's paying whom? And once you've done that, you can more clearly identify the motivations behind various decisions.

A Global Network Revealed. Langemann presents "a document that is unique... and which for the first time shows you the complex network of (worldwide) relationships, from non-governmental organizations (NGOs), companies, documents, and people." His 170-page essay describes more than 7,200 links between 6,500 entities and objects, including payment flows and investments.

Langemann says, "In the case of the Bill & Melinda Gates Foundation, already on page 4 of the document, you see that this foundation spent $43 billion [note that is billion with a "b"] in the U.S. alone... from 1994 to 2001, and distributed around half a billion dollars in Germany during this period"

The link to download the document is here.1 It is mostly in English. It describes a global network that covertly influences global health, finance, and governance.

The manuscript was created using software used by investigators and detectives use to identify hidden links between suspects. All the data, including documents, payment data, and the rest are public.

Red arrows are used throughout the document to indicate money flows, such as grants, donations, and other payments. As one example, as shown on page 3, at least 21 U.S. universities are financed by just three key organizations:

1. The Bill & Melinda Gates Foundation
2. The Open Philanthropy Project, a research and grantmaking foundation that is linked to the WEF
3. The Wellcome Trust, the world's second-largest health foundation, located in the U.K.

A Small Tight-Knit Group. According to the anonymous IT specialist who created the document, the core of this "COVID criminal network," is no larger than 20 or 30 people. Several of them appear on page 36, and their influence is phenomenal.

Many of these people met on May 8, 2019, at a political party event. They discussed how to strengthen global health and implement the United Nations Sustainable Development Goals. It was at a gathering of a political alliance of two German parties, the Christian Democratic Union of Germany (CDU) and the Christian Social Union in Bavaria (CSU). Attendees included:

Hermann Gröhe, Christian Democration Union (CDU) member and former Minister of Health

Ralph Brinkhaus, Parliamentary leader of the CDU

Dr. Angela Merkel, former Chancellor of Germany and a CDU member

Ilona Kickbush, Ph.D., Graduate Institute of International and Development Studies, Geneva

Tedros Adhanom Ghebreyesus, Director-General of the WHO

Dr. Christian Drosten, a German virologist who in early 2020 created the COVID PCR test

Dr. Clarissa Prazeres da Costa, microbiologist and infectious disease specialist

Joe Cerrell, managing director for Europe, the Middle East, and East Asia for The Gates Foundation

Professor Jeremy Farrar, director of the Wellcome Trust

Dr. Georg Kippels, CDU member

Jens Spahn, CDU member and a former Minister of Health

These individuals are found again and again working in overlapping groups.

For example, three of them were all present at a February 14, 2019, tabletop exercise on International Response to Deliberate Biological Events, held at the Munich Security Conference, as shown on page 124. Individuals from the Robert Koch Institute, the Chinese CDC, and the Gates Foundation were also present.

In 2017 and 2018, the same three were added as members to the International Advisory Board on Global Health. Two of them also joined the Global Preparedness Monitoring Board, a joint arm of the WHO and the World Bank, formally launched in May 2018. (Fauci is another member of this board.) Two other key persons within this network are:

·   Dr. Chris Elias, president of the Global Development Program at the Gates Foundation. He is on both the Global Preparedness Monitoring Board and the International Advisory Board on Global Health, together with the three others above.

·   Dr. Peter Piot, a Belgian-British microbiologist known for his research into Ebola and AIDS, a professor of global health, director of the London School of Hygiene and Tropical Medicine, a senior fellow with the Gates Foundation's Global Health Program, and former undersecretary-general with the United Nations.

Key Organizations. Due to the complexity of the network connections, there's no easy way to summarize them. You simply have to go through the document, page by page. That said, key organizations, whose networking connections are detailed, include:

- The Bill & Melinda Gates Foundation
- The Wellcome Trust, an organization funded by and strategically linked to GlaxoSmithKline (a vaccine maker in which Bill Gates is financially invested)
- The World Health Organization
- The Rockefeller Foundation
- The World Bank Group
- The World Economic Forum (WEF)
- GAVI, the Vaccine Alliance, founded by the Gates Foundation
- Coalition for Epidemic Preparedness Innovations (CEPI), founded by the governments of Norway and India, the Gates Foundation, the Wellcome Trust and WEF
- The Global Fund
- Forum of Young Global Leaders, founded by WEF in 2004
- FIND, the global alliance for diagnostics, seeks to ensure equitable access to reliable diagnosis around the world
- Big Pharma companies
- Johns Hopkins University
- Charité, Universitätsmedizin Berlin
- The Robert Koch Institute

- The European Commission
- The European Medicines and Healthcare Products Regulatory Agency (MHRA)
- The Swiss Agency for Therapeutic Products
- The German Global Health Hub

Of these, The Bill & Melinda Gates Foundation appears to be the most important element of this criminal network. Gates is also a major funder of mainstream media which, of course, is important if you want to ensure good press.

Gates' Media Control. In the past, the Bill & Melinda Gates Foundation funded the placement of "educational" messages in popular TV shows such as "ER," "Law & Order: SVU" and "Private Practice," including topics such as HIV prevention, surgical safety and the spread of infectious diseases, i.e., vaccinations.[2] But that was only the beginning.

Using more than 30,000 grants, Gates has contributed at least $319 million to the media, including CNN, NBC, NPR, PBS, The Atlantic, Texas Tribune (U.S.), the BBC, The Guardian, The Financial Times, The Daily Telegraph (U.K.), Le Monde (France), Der Spiegel (Germany), El País (Spain), and global broadcasters like Al-Jazeera.[3]

Also, more than $38 million of Gates' money has been funneled to investigative journalism centers. The majority of that money has gone into developing and expanding media in Africa.[4] Gates' donations come with strings attached. As reported by Columbia Journalism Review:[5]

"When Gates gives money to newsrooms, it restricts how the money is used — often for topics, like global health and education, on which the foundation works — which can help elevate its agenda in the news media.

For example, in 2015 Gates gave $383,000 to the Poynter Institute, a widely cited authority on journalism ethics ... earmarking the funds 'to improve the accuracy in worldwide media of claims related to global health and development.' Poynter senior vice president Kelly McBride said Gates's money was passed on to media fact-checking sites...

Since 2000, the Gates Foundation has given NPR $17.5 million [now up to $24.6 million6] through 10 charitable grants — all of them earmarked for coverage of global health and education, specific issues on which Gates works."

Who Else Controls the Media? Gates' power over the media is immense, but he's not the sole actor. Other players include BlackRock and the Vanguard Group, the two largest asset management firms in the world. They also control Big Pharma.7 Since they also own the media, you don't hear about their nearly universal monopoly. As noted in the video, "The Puppet Masters Portfolios," Vanguard and Blackrock:8

"... own the news that's been created, they own the distribution of the news that's been created, they own the lives of the reporters that are reporting the news that's being distributed... CBS, FOX, ABC, it doesn't matter which you're watching."

Conventional media are under the control of powerful influences, and their primary goal is not to give you objective information. Bill Gates, BlackRock, and Vanguard are furthering their agendas.

Who Owns the World? BlackRock and Vanguard also own shares in an impossibly long list of nearly every major company in the world. Aside from world media, the companies controlled by Blackrock and Vanguard span everything from entertainment and airlines to social media and communications.

Together, they form a hidden monopoly on global assets. And through their influence over our centralized media, they manipulate and control many of the world's events, economics, and how we view it all.

BlackRock and Vanguard have ownership in about 1,600 American firms. These had combined revenues of $9.1 trillion in 2015. Together with the third-largest global owner, State Street, their combined assets are nearly 90% of all S&P 500 firms.10

Vanguard holds a large share of Blackrock. In turn, Blackrock has been called the "fourth branch of government" by Bloomberg because they are the only private firm with financial agreements to lend money to the central banking system.11

Owners and stockholders of Vanguard include Rothschild Investment Corp,12 Edmond De Rothschild Holding,13 the Italian Orsini family, the American Bush family, the British Royal family, the du Pont family, and the Morgan, Vanderbilt, and Rockefeller families.

Gates Dictates Global Food Policy As Well. In addition to his grip on global health and media, Bill Gates' network also includes global food and agricultural policy. He's one of the largest farmland owners in the U.S.16

Gates is a longtime proponent of GMOs and toxic agricultural chemicals, and he's also gone on record urging Western nations to switch to synthetic lab-grown imitation beef. He also has lobbied against legislative efforts to be sure fake meats are properly labeled since that would slow down public acceptance.17

Not surprisingly, Gates is financially invested in most of his proposed "solutions" to the world's problems. These include hunger, disease, viral pandemics, and climate change.18

These kinds of self-serving endeavors have earned Gates the unofficial title of the most dangerous philanthropist in the world. As noted by AGRA Watch,19 Vandana Shiva, Ph.D., and others, Gates' philanthropy creates several new problems for each one he promises to solve. His work is best described as "philanthro-capitalism."

Again and again, Gates' globalist approach to farming has had devastating consequences for food and environmental sustainability and local food security. It is profitable for Gates and his corporate allies, though, and furthers the technocratic plan to control the world by owning all the resources.

The WEF, founded by technocrat figurehead Klaus Schwab, is one of several global nongovernmental agencies that help promote Gates' destructive agricultural and fake food agenda.

The Great Reset of Life as We Know It. The Gates Foundation, through its funding of the WEF, also plays an important role in The Great Reset. This was officially unveiled during a WEF summit in May 2020. As reported by The Defender, the Great Reset:20 "... is a vision for transferring the world into a totalitarian and authoritarian surveillance state manipulated by technocrats to manage traumatized populations, to shift wealth upward, and serve the interests of elite billionaire oligarchs."

Every conceivable aspect of life and society is scheduled to be "reset" according to their plan. This includes global food policies. Leading that charge is an organization called the EAT Forum, cofounded by the Wellcome Trust, which describes itself as the "Davos for food."

The EAT Forum's largest initiative is called FReSH,

which aims to transform the food system. Project partners in this venture include Bayer, Cargill, Syngenta, Unilever, and Google. EAT also collaborates with nearly 40 city governments in Europe, Africa, Asia, North America, South America, and Australia, and helps the Gates-funded United Nations Children's Fund (UNICEF) create dietary guidelines.

The Gates Foundation, WEF, and Wellcome Trust are present in every global health, finance, media, environmental policy, and food organization. Tying it all together is The Great Reset plan, with its Fourth Industrial Revolution, which is another Schwab concoction. This is the transformation of humanity under internet connection and control.

That is where this criminal COVID enterprise is ultimately trying to take us. To prevent this dystopian nightmare from happening, we need to see these hidden networks.

We need to recognize that planning is happening and that decisions in widespread areas are being made with common goals. Widespread coordination is underway.

These people are networked, and this makes them powerful. Only public understanding of these networks gives us a chance of defeating them. Their goal is to "reset" and "rebuild" our civilization ("Build Back Better") into one they will own.

Chapter 45
Naomi Wolf: It's China, Stupid

China is at war with us despite our skin-to-skin economic intercourse. The Chinese Communist Party's (CCP) leaders are doing this to displace their peoples' anger about their internal financial disaster onto the US.

The Chinese are not creative forces or original thinkers. They steal patents and imitate ideas. Frontal confrontations and kinetic war outside her borders are not China's style, either. (Although she believes Taiwan is her's.) She undermines by spreading plagues—viral infections and subversive ideas—concocted initially in the West. The Chinese must import food to survive, so they are aggressively purchasing farms and other real estate worldwide. We see this in California.

Although the Chinese attacks are not physical warfare, they are still body blows for us. Wolf explains how the CCP is one of the spiders at the center of the Covid and vaccine web. Besides damaging and killing us with these bioweapons, they are slaying our children by supplying free fentanyl and methamphetamine to the Mexican cartels for US sale.

Although understanding the outlines of this subject is fundamental, this post is somewhat technical, so after reading the initial story, speed-read it for the general idea. Pick the narrative up at the end, scan the conclusion, and look in more detail at my source reference section.

Disclaimer; Despite China's involvement, I do not think that Wolf believes it is the prime mover. From what we know at this point, that seems to be the US Department of Defense and the CIA.

* * *

Sorry to Announce a Genocide by Naomi Wolf.

July 17, 2022. Audio HERE.

I was relaxing on our screened porch in our little cottage in the forest, feeling rather pleased with myself. It had been an arduous week of the usual combat for liberty, but there had been victories. The grass was dewy, and the birds were loud. The morning was glorious.

But I heard a "thump" about eight feet away from my head. I glanced behind me and saw the enormous ears and forehead of a brown bear. He was ducking insolently, clearly aware of me, and lowered himself behind the trash cans.

Robert Yoho, MD (ret)

Naomi Wolf is a prominent journalist and major
contributor.

I ran indoors, locked the door, and grabbed a weapon
from the hall closet. I found myself cowering and armed
with a BB gun in an upstairs bathroom. I peered fearfully
out the window and saw that the bear was thin but
massively muscled and maybe eight feet long. It looked
disoriented.

I sped into the upstairs bedroom and secured the
windows. The bear left the garbage cans and followed me
around the corner of the house. My heart pounded as I realized that he was not leaving. No matter where I went, he
continued pacing and circling.

I locked the flimsy bedroom door and called the sheriff's
office. They told me twice that they could do nothing and to
stay inside. I don't blame them. They have more serious
issues than a city lady trapped in her house by a bear.

The animal circled the walls of the house for over an
hour. Adrenaline poured through me. I wondered if I would
be mauled and eaten.

I was saved when friends of mine, Craig Klein, Reinette Senum, and Jamie Arrigo, finally drove down our wooded driveway and blew their car horns. I raced down the steps, never so happy to see people in my life. Reinette laughed at the sight of me still clutching my useless BB gun.

Why do I tell this story? Because that bear had been growing more and more comfortable coming out of the woods and more and more comfortable exploring our trash. As bear watchers say, he became "habituated." He was there because I had done nothing to stop him. He was there because I let him slowly take over. He was marking his territory and finally started stalking me.

This happened, but that does not mean it is not also a metaphor.

SUBSTACK LINK

That week, I finalized my reports about the Pfizer vaccines. I had known for months that I would eventually uncover the following.

I had been reading reports produced by the medical and scientific experts of the WarRoom/DailyClout Pfizer Documents Research team. These 3000 volunteer experts were evaluating the 55,000 Pfizer documents that were released under court order.

By the end of my review, I knew that the situation was not just medicine gone wrong and not just a greedy pharmaceutical company with corrupted regulatory agencies. I was witness to a massive act of war.

I reviewed the eighteen months of sudden deaths, slow deaths, encephalitis, stroke, heart attacks, pericarditis, myocarditis, Guillain Barre syndrome, Bell's palsy, MS, blood clots, lung clots, leg clots, blue-green breast milk, spontaneous abortions, stillbirths, neonatal seizures, neonatal multi-organ system failure, liver damage, kidney damage, suppressed lactation, decreased sperm count, and disrupted menses described in the Pfizer documents. I saw that 34,000 of the 42,000 "adverse events" tabulated during the worldwide rollout of the Pfizer injections were from the US. I saw that the next largest group was from Western Europe and that the other 56 countries using the Pfizer injections had only a bit over 7000 adverse events. I knew then that I was viewing not just medicine gone wrong on a massive scale but rather an act of war.

I saw a doubling of neonatal deaths and a 34% increase in stillbirths and spontaneous abortions for vaccinated mothers in country after country. I saw that 3816 vaccinated women in the VAERS database lost their babies. I saw that these were 57% of all neonatal deaths for all vaccines for the entire time that VAERS records had been kept. I saw that of the 36 pregnancies described in the Pfizer documents, 28 of the fetuses died. And I also saw the 40 percent rise in overall death rates and the shocking increase in disabilities in the West. I knew then that I was not seeing medicine gone wrong on a massive scale but an act of war.

I learned that the damage and lethality caused by the injections could be boosted by increasing the concentration of the solution and that the brands had different amounts of the active ingredient. Moderna, with its 100 mcg dose, is far more damaging than Pfizer, with 30 mcg. I knew that I was seeing not just medicine gone wrong on a massive scale but an act of war.

I saw a study out of Hong Kong from 2021. The authors, of course, were answerable to the Chinese Communist Party (CCP). This revealed that a second dose into the bloodstreams of mice resulted in visibly enlarged hearts with white patches that were visible to the naked eye. The animals also had cytokine storms and liver damage. I realized then that the two-dose regime and "boosters" were progressive methods to damage and destroy the health of Westerners. The study concluded, "Post-vaccination myopericarditis is reported after immunization with coronavirus disease 2019 (COVID-19) messenger RNA (mRNA) vaccines."

REFERENCE: Intravenous Injection of Coronavirus Disease 2019 (COVID-19) mRNA Vaccine Can Induce Acute Myopericarditis in Mouse Model. The authors, of course, are Chinese. Clinical Infectious Diseases, Volume 74, Issue 11, 1 June 2022, Pages 1933–1950,

We were told that Pfizer/BioNTech was a German company, but it is actually a German-Chinese company. I learned that this corporation had a memorandum of understanding (MOU) with Fosun Pharmaceuticals, a major CCP-linked pharmaceutical company based in Shanghai, to make the Pfizer/BioNTech mRNA vaccines. I knew that with a bit more digging, I would find China at the heart of these acts of war.

BioNTech's SEC filing shows that the MOU with Fosun Pharmaceuticals includes an equity investment by

Fosun in BioNTech. In other words, the CCP is an equity investor in BioNTech.

> As part of the strategic alliance with Shanghai Fosun Pharmaceutical (Group) Co., Ltd ("Fosun Pharma"... whereby the two companies will work together on the development of BNT162 in China, Fosun agreed to make an equity investment which was received in mid-April 2020. The issuance of 1,580,777 ordinary shares with the nominal amount of k€ 1,581 was registered within the commercial register (Handelsregister) as of April 23, 2020... [Ai-Min Hui, President of Global R&D, and Chief Medical Officer of Fosun Pharma said] We are closely working with BioNTech and regulatory authorities to evaluate the safety and efficacy of the vaccine candidate, to synchronize the development process in China with other countries, and to bring the vaccine to the public as soon as possible, if the vaccine succeeds.

And so, Fosun is not separate from the CCP; it is the CCP. Fosun acquired almost half of Sinopharm.
SOURCES
1) In 2003, Fosun Pharmaceutical acquired a 49% stake in Sinopharm Group (Chinese: 国药控股)... In 2008, a year before the initial public offering of Sinopharm Group, Fosun Pharmaceutical owned the direct parent company of Sinopharm Group, Sinopharm Industrial Investment (Chinese: 国药产业投资) instead; the majority owner of the joint venture was state-owned China National Pharmaceutical Group(Sinopharm).
2) FROM: 2003年年报 [2003 Annual Report] (PDF). Fosun Industrial. 24 April 2004. Retrieved 5 August 2018–

via Shanghai Stock Exchange website. [^ 国药集团复星联合成立首家混合所有制药企. 企业观察报 (in Chinese (China)). 4 August 2014. Retrieved 5 August 2018 – via Sina; ^ 2009年年报 [2009 Annual Report] (PDF). Fosun Pharmaceutical. 25 March 2010. Retrieved 5 August 2018 – via Shanghai Stock Exchange website.; ^ "Connection Transaction" (PDF) (Press release). Shanghai: Fosun International. 20 June 2008.

Sinopharm, of course, as you see now, of which Fosun owns almost half, is owned directly by the Chinese state and thus reports directly to the CCP.

The initial BioNTech/Fosun MOU seems to imply that all of the BioNTech/Fosun joint ventures' activity is in China, or in regions aligned with or close to China. But Fosun Pharma did not stay in China—it came here. Fosun Pharmaceuticals is now also Fosun Pharmaceuticals USA, with branches for R and D and product formulation in Boston, MA and Princeton, NJ.

It now produces products in the US for distribution here and around the world. Fosun Pharma has built a "global operation strategy" for the manufacture of COVID-19 vaccines, COVID-19 PCR tests and COVID-19 antigen tests. The following is from the Fosun website:

> Fosun Pharma has built a strong root in China and developed a global operation strategy, with pharmaceutical manufacturing and R&D being the largest and core business segment....
>
> In 2021, the revenue from new and sub-new products including COMIRNATY® (mRNA COVID-19 vaccine, also known as BNT162b2)... accounted for over 25% of the revenue in the pharmaceutical manufacturing segment; Revenue from regions outside Mainland China

and countries overseas reached RMB13,599 million, accounting for 34.86% of the total revenue, marking a step forward on globalization.

...Continuously strengthening the global operation capability and making further enhancement for globalization, Fosun Pharma has formed a global operating system for R&D, manufacturing and commercialization, and continuously expands overseas markets... The second headquarters in the United States help to build a global business landscape with full coverage of R&D, manufacturing and commercialization...

By the end of 2021, Fosun Pharma's overseas commercialization team with over 1,200 employees has built marketing platforms in the United States, Africa and Europe and has achieved direct sales of formulations to the U.S. market... The COVID-19 test kit by Fosun Diagnostics has been sold in over ten countries... Gland Pharma, a holding subsidiary in India, received approvals from the US FDA for 13 generic drugs in 2021.

Leveraging the current global manufacturing capability and world-class manufacturing facilities... Fosun Pharma has accelerated the acquirement of international GMP certification of domestic production lines, laying a solid foundation for exporting domestic products. In January and March 2022, Fosun Pharmaceutical Industrial obtained the Medicines Patent Pool (MPP)'s license to produce and supply the generic version of Merck's oral COVID-19 treatment Molnupiravir and Pfizer's oral COVID-19 treatment Nirmatrelvir, as well as the co-packaged product of Nirmatrelvir and Ritonavir of Pfizer... The license includes both ingredients and the finished drug.

Cassandra's Memo

Fosun Pharma USA offers potential partners: "A global reach with a focus on the United States and China markets". It offers "US Rights," "Global Rights," as well as "China Rights."

The FDA Filing for the Fosun Pharma USA facility says the facility is authorized to "develop specifications," including for the PCR and antigen tests it creates, and that the facility can also have US agents.

This is crucial. Fosun Pharmaceuticals did not just partner with Pfizer/BioNTech to make the COVID-19 vaccines. They make the PCR tests that are the one primary measure to determine the pandemic's scale in North America and Western Europe. This dictates the "lock-downs" of entire countries and industrial sectors.

Therefore, a CCP-run company and CCP-created product decide who can go to work or school, who must close their shop, and who can or cannot travel in all of Europe and the US. A CCP-run company decides the formulation of the PCR and antigen tests that go deep into the nasopharynx of Westerners who are forced, week after week, to test and test and test with these products.

From the Fosun Pharma USA's product pages:

FOSUN COVID-19 RT-PCR DETECTION KIT

FDA Emergency Use Authorization (EUA) Only
Rx Only
For In Vitro Diagnostic Use.

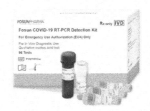

— COVID-19 RT_PCR

Covid-19 RT-PCR Detection Kit Targeting Three Genes

The Fosun COVID-19 RT-PCR Detection Kit is a real-time RT-PCR test intended for the qualitative detection of nucleic acid from the SARS-CoV-2 in upper and lower respiratory specimens (such as anterior nasal swabs, mid-turbinate nasal swabs, nasopharyngeal swabs, oropharyngeal swabs, sputum, lower respiratory tract aspirates, bronchoalveolar lavage, and nasopharyngeal wash/aspirate or nasal aspirate) from individuals suspected of COVID-19 by their healthcare provider. The kit detects ORF1ab, N and the E genes of the SARS-CoV-2 virus. Testing is limited to laboratories certified under the Clinical Laboratory Improvement Amendments (CLIA) of 1988, 42 U.S.C. §263a, to perform high complexity tests.

— About FDA Emergency Use Authorization (EUA)

EMERGENCY USE AUTHORIZATION
(EUA GRANTED BY THE FDA)

This test (1) has not been FDA cleared or approved, (2) has been authorized by FDA under an EUA for use by authorized laboratories, (3) has been authorized only for the detection of nucleic acid from SARS-CoV-2, not for any other viruses or pathogens, and (4) is only authorized for the duration of the declaration that circumstances exist justifying the authorization of emergency use of in vitro diagnostics for detection and/or diagnosis of COVID-19 under Section 564(b)(1) of the Act, 21 U.S.C. § 360bbb-3(b)(1), unless the authorization is terminated or revoked sooner.

Products

Product Name	Catalog Number	Package Quantity	
Fosun COVID-19 RT-PCR Detection Kit	PCSYHF03-a	96 Tests/Kit	Order Info Request Form

Components

- SARS-COV-2 Reaction Reagent
- RT-PCR Enzyme
- Positive Control of SARS-CoV-2
- Negative Control
- Internal Reference A

Resources

- Healthcare Provider Fact Sheet (HCP)
- Patient Fact Sheet (Patient)
- Instructions for Use (IFU)
- Symbols Glossary

- Limit of Detection | 300 copies/mL
- Instrument | Applied Biosystems 7500
- Storage & Shelf Life | -25° C to -15° C with protection from light, 12 months

Features

- 3 Targets | ORF1ab, N and E genes
- Sample Types* | Including Nasopharyngeal swab, Oropharyngeal swab, Sputum
- Amplification Time | 1 hour 20 minutes
- Controls | Internal control, UNG enzyme and dUTP used to reduce risk of contamination, false positive and false negative results

*Upper and lower respiratory specimens such as anterior nasal swabs, mid-turbinate nasal swabs, nasopharyngeal swabs, oropharyngeal swabs, sputum, lower respiratory tract aspirates, bronchoalveolar lavage, and nasopharyngeal wash/aspirate or nasal aspirate.

SOURCE: The following products are developed at the Princeton, New Jersey Fosun Pharma USA facility:

QJR	FOSUN PHARMA USA INC.	Fosun COVID-19 RT-PCR Detection Kit	2020-04-19
QKO	FOSUN PHARMA USA INC.	Fosun COVID-19 IgG/IgM Rapid Antibody Detection Kit	2020-04-17
KXG	FOSUN PHARMA USA INC.	Nasopharyngeal Swab	2020-04-11

This CCP-owned hybrid entity is here and is creating the diagnostics that determine the scale of the pandemic in the West. The CCP can dial the whole thing up or down.

It also makes millions of Pfizer/BioNTech mRNA injections, the Merck COVID-19 pill Molnupiravir, and the Pfizer COVID-19 pill Paxlovid. Pfizer CEO Albert Bourla just signed a contract in 2022 with the US government for 10 million doses and $5.29 billion dollars for the US and for ten other countries including the EU.

All this is formulated and distributed by a company leading directly to the Chinese Communist Party.

When Biden does a deal with Pfizer/BioNTech for millions of dollars using our tax money, he is giving a substantial portion of the funds to China. When he spends a billion dollars via omnibus bills for personal protective equipment, including millions for PCR and antigen tests, he is writing checks to China.

SOURCE

From Fosun Pharmaceutical USA's website section "Research and Development." See the last three entries:

Therapeutic Area	Project	Target/MOA	Indication
Nervous System	Opicapone Tablet	COMT	Parkinson's syndromes
Blood System	Avatrombopag Tablet	TPO-R	Chronic idiopathic thrombocytopenic purpura
	Tenapanor Tablet	NHE 3	End-stage Renal Disease – Hemodialysis
	Ferric Pyrophosphate Citrate	-	Iron replacement for HD patients
Metabolism and Digestive System	Tenapanor Tablet	NHE 3	Irritable Bowel Syndrome with Constipation
	FCN-207	URAT1	Hyperuricemia / Gout
	FCN-342	URAT1	Gout
Infectious Diseases	Molnupiravir	RNA polymerase	Treatment of COVID-19
	Paxlovid	3CL Protease	Treatment of COVID-19
	mRNA vaccine BNT162b2	-	Immunization to prevent COVID-19

Is Fosun a squeaky clean CCP-run Pharma enterprise? In 2018 a whistleblower — and in China, that is a courageous thing to be — broke a scandal revealing that Fosun Pharmaceuticals had "massively" faked its data and bribed regulators. Facilities were so chaotic that the US FDA sent the company a stern warning letter.

BioNTech's SEC filing reports a tech transfer to China. Not to a "Chinese company" or a "Chinese individual" but to the country of China.

Further, the SEC filing explains that it will effect "technology transfer with China" after granting marketing approval. I don't know what "technology transfer" or "tech transfer" means in this SEC filing. The experts who reviewed it for me suggested that it can mean internet protocol, manufacturing methodologies, formulas, data, or all four.

BioNTech declared as 100 % complete or in process, a "tech transfer" to CHINA. It is not "sharing" the tech or "licensing" the tech — it is transferring the tech. That means that in some capacity, China will be or is in charge of some aspect of BioNTech's technology, however that is defined here.

Consider all the above together with the 150,000 plus adverse events in the Pfizer documents, the deadly harms to reproduction, the Western baby die-off, and the babies with seizures. Consider the population drop and the rise in disabilities. Consider the rigid, cruel vaccine mandates aimed at Western defense forces: Canada's, Australia's, all of Western Europe's, as well as the most powerful military in the world, that of the United States. Consider the vaccine mandates aimed at our police, our healthcare workers, our firefighters, our pilots, our first responders, our kids, and our babies.

All this was done by a White House that was captive to the CCP via Hunter Biden's laptop. Add to all this the 12 to 30 percent decline in birth rates now showing up in countries still keeping real statistics around the world.

How better to cripple the world's other superpower than by destroying our American front lines and our American next generation with tainted, murderous vaccines? How easy to do the same to Western Europe, Canada, and Australia? This all flows into the West through a few shell companies. The vaccine's CCP and Pharma origins reveal the core methodology of this warfare.

Take all of the above and add that the virus originated in China. Also consider that all of the testing apparatuses, millions of vaccines, and the catastrophically damaging or lethal "solutions" to the virus all originated there as well. This is the same leadership that brought the world forced abortions, organ harvesting, citizens welded into their homes, and Uyghur concentration camps.

We have let our adversaries come too close to us. These include the World Economic Forum, the World Health Organization, the Bill and Melinda Gates Foundation, the tech companies, and the Chinese Communist Party. My new book *The Bodies of Others* describes how this transnational group of evil actors used the pandemic to crush humanity and destroy the West.

We are staring into the abyss, so we must snap out of denial. We must turn and face the ravening beast and save each other.

Author Naomi Wolf is one of the most inspirational figures in the freedom movement, and my respect for her is boundless. The above is from her Substack Outspoken. Her team analyzed the Pfizer data dump, which was a massive, cooperative achievement. HERE, HERE, and HERE are other posts of hers. Her website is DailyClout.io.

China is a spouse who never accepted us, has been working against us from the start, and is now feeding us poisons.

Other sources

- To see concentration camps and other networks of control being built, see China in Five Tweets HERE.
- Peter and Ginger Breggin's *Covid 19 and the Global Predators: We Are the Prey* is one of the most complete sources.
- Sam Quinones wrote *THE LEAST OF US: True Tales of America and Hope in the Time of Fentanyl and Meth.*
- From an *Asia Media* article, The China-Mexico Connection, "Cartels can 'stamp fentanyl into pills' so that they resemble prescription drugs like Adderall and Xanax. According to the DEA, two out of five of these fake pills contain potentially lethal doses of fentanyl."

From a *Newsmax* article, Chinese Working With Mexican Cartels to Get Fentanyl to US, "We're dealing with the Chinese... Communist Party; they are organizing the fentanyl shipments to Mexico. At some level, they are involved in manufacturing, and doing it with the goal of killing American kids... And then they're having Chinese students in the U.S. pick up the [drug] money."

According to El Pais, a disturbing trend is developing, with fentanyl seizures reaching record-high levels while a new version of the drug, rainbow fentanyl, is drawing concern among U.S. authorities... The colorful drug "looks like candy." In mid-August, Customs and Border Protection found more than 250,000 pills in a vehicle entering the U.S. through Mexico. A day later, over 15,000 rainbow fentanyl pills were found [on] a person detained at the Nogales, Arizona, border crossing.

Chapter 46
Diversions (you need it):
Winnie the Pooh, Piglet, and
Others

Winnie the Pooh and Piglet are puzzled.

Piglet was clearing snow from the front of his house, and Pooh was walking around in a circle nearby. They try to trace the footprints back, but there seem to be more of them each time. They soon spot a second set of smaller tracks, and Piglet gets afraid and leaves. Christopher Robin explains to Pooh how they had been going in circles following their own footprints.

The charm of Pooh is that children listening to the stories figure out the problems before the teddy bear does.

Not even the psychopaths devising and committing genocide are sure what will happen next. No one has ever perpetrated global atrocities like these, and the conspirators must be looking for omens in the snow like the rest of us. We have allowed agencies, governments, corporations, and individuals to carry out such evil acts over recent decades that they have escalated to killing our children. There is no way back for these monsters—their bestiality has been laid bare.

Be patient with yourself—I, too, am shocked anew every week.

* * *

The polymath perspective

Victor Davis Hansen, of the Hoover institute and author of hundreds of books about warfare and the classics, says that American structures are tottering yet still standing. He explains why we will survive and how our future may play out HERE. If you like him, HERE are more of his videos. I listen at double speed.

* * *

A cry for help from a 70-year-old physician friend living in Dubai.

Hi Bob,

I wanted to tell you about my experiences with the destructive effects of the Covid vaccine on me.

1. I was vaccinated twice with AstraZeneca due to pressure from my family. I did not take a booster.

2. Despite having normal blood pressure, blood sugars (on Metformin), normal cholesterol (on statins), and Eliquis (blood thinner), on February 9th, I woke up with severe chest pain around 7 AM.

3. The ambulance was in my bedroom within 10 minutes

4. My cardiogram showed an ST-elevation heart attack (N.B.: a severe type that is frequently fatal)

5. I was rushed to the hospital, and my cardiologist was already waiting for me

6. Cardiac stents were used to open my coronary arteries within an hour

7. I saw the blood flow return immediately. The ST elevation and pain went away

8. My troponin (heart enzyme) was zero after one week

9. I was back to work after one week

PS: My hearing has deteriorated dramatically since the vax. I now have trouble living without a hearing aid. My staff has to shout for me to hear them.

Best regards, Rashid

My reply:

R— Jeez, you were lucky. You knew the truth from my emails, yet you bowed to your idiot relatives. You now know why I call it the clot shot.

You damaged your immunity by getting jabbed, so your chances of dying from Covid and other causes are now higher. Vax damage involves multiple organ systems—heart, brain, and circulatory system. It causes general inflammatory conditions such as cancer that may begin years later. Many people close to me have died, and some have had terrible strokes. Your experience is not unique.

Well, I don't want to lose you. Ignore the advice of jackasses from now on.

My best, Robert

* * *

My blue-pill friends

Until recently, I was angry and had lost all respect for them. The facts were well documented, and they refused to "get it." I thought, "You cannot wake someone pretending to be asleep."

Robert Yoho, MD (ret)

(Creative commons photo)

I wondered if they were either bribed—corrupt—or cowardly. Some of them seemed to have been fooled because they were stupid. But a lot of the smart ones were deceived along with the rest. They were what they were eating, and they were chewing propaganda all day long.

For example, I have (had) a dear friend who works at a top US university and hangs out with people who have IQs over 160. But she has never glimpsed the Matrix. After suffering through 70 of my posts, she wrote, "You're sick. I hope you get the help you need. Don't reply; just unsubscribe me." She must have been reading my writing as I-feel-sorry-for-you porn.

I am also close to an influential foreign country leader I will call John. To his credit, he is savvier than his advisors and wears skepticism like a suit of armor. He told me, reasonably enough, that I worry too much. But he also said that the World Economic Forum consists of powerless idiots who get together and just talk. He also believes that Covid is a deadly peril and that we were helpless before the vaccine. Lately, he has been worrying about—wait for it —monkeypox.

I have known John for decades, and his integrity is bulletproof. I could not believe that he would respond to threats or could be paid off. When I spent a few days with him recently, I was reminded that he left the TV on all day and realized he was hypnotized. Like so many others, he is what he is exposed to. Watching mainstream media turns people into walking CNNs, and they parrot propaganda.

Somehow, despite everything I sent and said to these people, neither listened.

* * *

Tolkien described the first banker in *The Hobbit:*

> [After Smaug slaughtered all the dwarves], he took their wealth for himself. Probably, for that is the dragons' way, he has piled it all up in a great heap far inside and sleeps on it for a bed. (He lay there), a vast red-golden dragon, fast asleep; a thrumming came from his jaws and nostrils, and wisps of smoke, but his fires were low in slumber. Beneath him, under all his limbs and his huge coiled tail, and about him on all sides stretching away across the unseen floors, lay countless piles of precious things, gold wrought and unwrought, gems and jewels, and silver red-stained in the ruddy light. Smaug lay, with wings folded like an immeasurable bat, turned partly on one side, so that the hobbit could see his underparts and his long pale belly crusted with gems and fragments of gold from his long lying on his costly bed. Behind him where the walls were nearest could

dimly be seen coats of mail, helms, and axes, swords and spears hanging; and there in rows stood great jars and vessels filled with a wealth that could not be guessed.

After executing genocide on every living creature around him, Smaug fell when a courageous archer's shaft pierced a tiny weakness in his belly armor.

Part Eleven
Lawyers, Guns, and Money

Chapter 47
Lawyers: The Latest From Florida is Richard Fleming's Idea

I come back to you now, at the turn of the tide.

— Gandalf

Excerpted from Jeff Childer's substack HERE, December 14, 2022.
In the first week of October, Florida became the first official government entity to recommend against the vaccines — for any reason. It also became the first government entity to break the chains of slavery to that grotesque abomination called the Centers for Disease Control, which is more dangerous than any disease, and start doing its own independent research.

Now, not even three months later, while pharaoh Biden was distracted dancing with drag queens in the White House, Florida — like the ancient Israelites — just left Egypt.

In case you missed all the hoopla yesterday, and somehow overlooked the ultra-rare C&C Breaking News alert (shame on you), yesterday Governor DeSantis hosted the scientific roundtable we've been fervently praying for.

The short version is, Florida is about to do four incredibly significant things:

- *Convene a statewide criminal Grand Jury to investigate crimes and fraud committed against Floridians related to the covid-19 vaccines. I am* NOT *making that up!*
- *Establish a "Public Health Integrity Committee," overseen by its Harvard-trained Surgeon General, which will assess all federal public health recommendations and guidance, to ensure that Florida's public health policies are good for Florida. In other words, we're not slavishly following the CDC anymore.*
- *Work with medical examiners to study autopsy results of all Floridians who died suddenly after receiving the covid-19 vaccine. The state will also work with the University of Florida to compare its research to studies from other countries.*
- *Introduce a new bill over the next few weeks designed to protect physicians' independent judgment, their First Amendment rights, and their independent right to dissent from orthodox narratives.*

* * *

RICHARD FLEMING, JD, MD, Ph.D., has been trying to get this action going for over a year.

Dr. Fleming is a physicist. They regard the rest of science as stamp collecting and are likely right. I watched him speak for three hours during a 2022 meeting in Sacramento and interviewed him for my podcast in December 2022. Fleming says we have little time. He speculates that the criminals running the game will soon manufacture another crisis.

He is ready to present criminal cases against Gates, Fauci, and the other US citizens who have murdered over a million Americans. Fleming chose his defendants because they were the ones most likely to rat out the others and expand the prosecution. As a prosecutor'ss saying goes, "The first to squeal gets the best deal." He outlines the relentless process that will occur once a few state Attorney Generals (AGs) stand up. Dr. Fleming also explains his legal strategies and interprets recent events. He has a pre-recorded deposition on his website HERE.

Please go to flemingmethod.com or 10letters.org to help out. We are asking you to send printed copies of the recommended documents to your state AGs and governors, plus ten (10) of your friends. Dr. Fleming said they are under pressure to move cases like this off their desks and get them to the next step. If you help, this action will spread exponentially.

SUBSTACK LINK December 2022 interview

Chapter 48
Guns: Are You a Sheep, a Wolf, or a Knight?

And each man stands with his face in the light. Of his own drawn sword, ready to do what a hero can.

— Elizabeth Barrett Browning

Only three types of people live in our world—the knights, the sheep, and the wolves. The knights, such as the police, defend us. The wolves are thieves, armed robbers, violent offenders, and now government agencies. Sheep are preyed upon by wolves and need knights to protect them.

Social unrest is inevitable when fixed incomes meet hyperinflation If you close your eyes to this, your behavior and beliefs make you a victim and embolden wolves.

You can learn a lot about violent crime from surveillance videos. YouTube's Active Self Protection (ASP) is a channel with footage from police, bystanders, and building security systems. John Correia, the host, supplies analysis. He will show you that law enforcement has a nearly impossible job and that they occasionally make mistakes. But when criminals threaten lives, the only solution may be to shoot them.

Correia has evaluated tens of thousands of videos from all over the world. Although some people with guns make mistakes and harm others, his numbers prove that civilian firearm possession results in better overall outcomes. Compliance with an armed robber gets you shot 25 percent of the time without a weapon, *but if you have a gun, this drops to 10 percent.*

ASP is part violence porn, but the channel offers many lessons and is addictive. Titles include "Defender uses roast chicken to stop a robber:" Others are "Elderly store owner fights off armed robbers" and "Family survives ambush machete attack." More samples are HERE, HERE, and HERE. Warning—you will see people who die a few moments later. Armed robbers threatening others with death deserve this.

The channel has many videos of gun carriers preventing crime. Some of these knights are off-duty police officers. Many retired police and military also carry firearms. Their background is comprehensive, and they afford us another layer of protection against criminals. If you think you have what it takes to be a defender, ASP is your first step. You must be a sane, sober, ethical person who gets training and studies local firearm laws.

The US Constitution requires all jurisdictions to allow concealed carry, and even Los Angeles County is being forced to become more permissive by a recent Supreme Court case. Certain other states are "Constitutional carry" or "open carry," which require less training and paperwork.

Robert Yoho, MD (ret)

SUBSTACK LINK

* * *

BASICS for beginners

Gun geeks quibble over advice like this, and in their defense, the issues are complex.

•Handgun carry has been simplified by Kydex plastic holsters that fit the gun on a heavy, stiff belt. This combination holds the weapon securely, but it can still be rapidly drawn. It snaps into the holster with a click, and as long as it is there, firing the gun is impossible. The holster shields the trigger so you can safely carry the gun with a bullet in the chamber. Leather holsters are less safe.

- The right gun, holster, and belt combination is surprisingly comfortable. Nexbelt is an incredible synthetic belt that, along with a holster, costs about $150.
- Because violent situations develop rapidly, the most effective strategy is to have the firearm on your person at all times for quick access. "Appendix carry" of the weapon on the front of the belt on the dominant-hand side is popular.

Your body type and needs dictate your choice, so study this issue.

- Glocks are the most popular handgun because of their reliability, simplicity, and ease of operation. Smaller ones are less than two pounds. They have no safety, but authorities consider this an advantage. The Kydex holsters are a reliable safety by themselves.

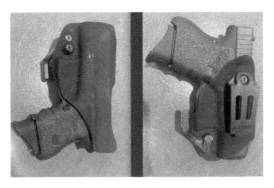

Glock 26 with grip extension magazine and Kydex holster that covers the trigger.

- Never point a firearm at anyone unless you mean to shoot! And never point it at yourself. Be especially careful when replacing the gun in the holster. If you get your clothing entangled, it could pull the trigger and shoot you in an embarrassing place.
- Keep your finger high and off the trigger unless you mean to shoot. This requires training.
- More than 80 percent of gun carriers, including police, use 9-millimeter ammunition. Several types of expanding bullets make this relatively small caliber powerful enough. Some defenders

prefer a bigger round, such as a .40 or a .45. These kick more, but if the target is struck, a single bullet may stop the threat.

- Non-lethal weapons such as pepper spray are essential, inexpensive tools, but firearms are the best option when criminals have potentially lethal methods.
- Tasers get the target under control only half the time. When they fail, it pisses off the person getting tased, which frequently worsens a bad situation. These weapons require training and are only reasonable for police.
- Some places allow open carry, but except for police, this is a mistake because it telegraphs the gun's location. The weapon can potentially be stolen and used against the owner.
- Training, study, and practice on the range are necessary to make you safe and effective.
- Never fire warning shots, and always shoot at the center of mass.
- Semi-automatics are modern weapons that automatically load another bullet when fired. Quality brands seldom jam. Revolvers or "wheel guns" are older, bulkier designs. Contrary to street mythology, extensive shooting range experience proves these are less reliable.
- The police cannot show up immediately. You need to be able to take care of yourself.
- Calling the police is usually the last resort. Law enforcement cannot read minds and must rely on their immediate perceptions of what they see and hear. For example, if you have a

relative or friend who always acts crazy but never hurts anyone, they might get shot if you dial 911.

- It is generally defensible to shoot someone threatening others with guns or other deadly force such as knives. But in some situations, showing others that you have a firearm is a crime called "brandishing."
- If you fire a gun, you will face legal consequences regardless of the circumstances.
- If you are involved in a shooting, and the police come, keep your hands in the air and tell them the location of any weapons.
- Never, ever make a detailed statement to police at the scene. Wait until later when you have an attorney present.
- Hardening your home's doors by beefing up the locks and installing long screws on the hinges discourages many robbers. Your local Home Depot or Lowe's can guide you. They have steel doors that practically require a tractor to open if locked. The nice ones are ornamental or look like ordinary screen doors. These are easily installed, and the cheapest ones only cost a few hundred dollars.

* * *

CRITICAL

You will have a better chance of protecting yourself and the people around you if you are knowledgeable and carry a weapon.

If you get into trouble with strangers, remember that 20

percent of the US populace is taking psych drugs. They may be unpredictable and are occasionally homicidal.

Always be prepared to apologize to drunken fools or those who lose their tempers in traffic. Never be concerned about whether you are right. Use the phrase I call the magic three: "You are right, I am wrong, and I am sorry." This also works wonderfully with spouses, even when you do not mean it—and sometimes when they know you do not mean it.

Self-protection is primarily about staying alert, being polite, avoiding trouble, and having the right attitude. And as John Correia says, "Don't go to stupid places, do stupid things, with stupid people, at stupid times of the night."

If you doubt that guns might someday be needed to defend our Constitutional freedoms, study the Warsaw Ghetto liquidation during World War II. Since the residents there had only a few firearms, they could only offer token resistance before they were packed off to extermination camps. In America, about 400 million guns are in the hands of 80 million armed citizens. Let us pray that we will never be called on to defend ourselves against our government with them.

Chapter 49
Money: Cautious Optimism About Bitcoin

The governments of the world have spent hundreds and hundreds of trillions of dollars bailing out a decaying, Dickensian, outmoded system called banking, when the solution to the future of finance is peer-to-peer. It's going to be alternative currencies like bitcoin and it's not actually going to be a banking system as we had before 2008.

— Patrick Young, Financial analyst

Bitcoin is an electronic currency invented in 2008 that is currently classified as a commodity like gold. This means that capital gains tax is due when it is sold. Its advocates say it can defeat the central bankers.

We know its structure is robust because it has been tested repeatedly by sophisticated hackers throughout its existence. If they could penetrate Bitcoin, their reward would be billions of dollars. Many serious people have worked for over a decade on Bitcoin's infrastructure, including the "wallets," "mining," and exchanges. Roughly 100 million people own Bitcoin.

The total number of Bitcoins is limited absolutely to 21 million, and this is locked into the source code. About 19 million exist now. Because this supply is restricted, the currency cannot inflate. This only works because Bitcoin is outside of banks and other central control. It exists in thousands of computers worldwide—the most massive computer network in history. Each coin is conveniently divisible into units of a hundred millionth, and there are now systems that work on top of Bitcoin that allow for even smaller parts.

Established theory says people hold more secure currencies and spend less secure ones. This means that the good ones cannibalize the inflating ones. This has so far proven true for Bitcoin, for its usage and price have increased for over a decade. Bitcoin is the best-growing asset class—ever— and has appreciated faster than any stock in history.

Hyperinflation destroys the economy along with money. For example, as the value of Venezuelan currency wasted away, shops inside the country could not get essentials and were left empty. The following chart shows what has happened to the dollar over the years as its value was purposely destroyed.

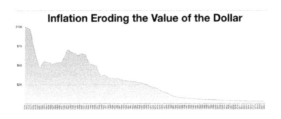

Inflation Eroding the Value of the Dollar

Gold has been used as money for millennia and is the oldest and best-recognized store of value. Bitcoin has many similar features and some that are superior. These include security, portability, and near-instant transferability. With real estate, these three assets are the most likely to hold value against inflation.

A simple technical analysis of scarcity called "stock to flow" is the ratio of the total stock of gold to the amount of new gold mined. Since Bitcoin is "mined" with computers just like gold is mined from the earth, this analysis can also be done for it. The results for the two assets are nearly identical.

Bitcoin's price volatility is worrisome, but its trading volume is in the top five exchangeable currencies world-wide. It is used for settlements that are trillions of dollars each year, and this increases year over year. Worldwide Bitcoin transfers are about the same as the huge Fedwire system. Their website says:

> [We are] the premier electronic funds-transfer service that banks, businesses and government agencies rely on for mission-critical, same-day transactions. Fedwire Funds Service participants benefit from the finality of payments credited to their Federal Reserve Bank master accounts.

Bitcoin has had no technical issues since 2013. Its development is slow, deliberate, and focused on security. Its secrecy is imperfect but being developed. China banned bitcoin mining in 2021, but around 20% of bitcoin's mining is estimated to still occur in China. This technology is hard to stamp out, even by authoritarian governments.

People in inflation-prone countries need help finding stores of value to save their money and investments. Many understand Bitcoin's promise instantly, for they know that their currencies are like melting ice cubes. On Chainalysis' crypto adoption index, 18 of the 20 top countries are developing countries. In notoriously corrupt Nigeria, for example, the central bank banned Bitcoin, but this is being ignored. They recently introduced a central bank digital currency, but it has yet to have much success against Bitcoin.

El Salvador and the Central African Republic have made Bitcoin legal tender. Saint Kitts and Nevis is getting close. Other countries peg their currencies to the US dollar or actually use it. Because of inflation, mimicking the dollar only works over the short term.

Bitcoin's market cap, the total value of it all, is $321.80 billion, down from $1.204 trillion a year ago. In comparison, all the gold in the world is worth about $12 trillion, and all stocks have a market cap of about $92 trillion. Many savvy investors are trying to get a small percentage of their holdings into Bitcoin. This serves both as an inflation hedge and has upside potential. Any portfolio with a few percent Bitcoin has had far better returns than most others over the past decade. If even one percent of all stock funds become Bitcoin, its price would soar.

There is a Bitcoin exchange-traded fund (ETF) on the Canadian stock exchange and several stock proxies for holding Bitcoin in the US. Alternatively, you can purchase Bitcoin directly from US exchanges such as Kraken, Swan Bitcoin, or Binance (lower fees) with wire transfers or sometimes credit cards. Bitcoin ATMs that change cash to bitcoin are in all major US and European cities. The commissions on these are high.

Scandals and scams plague Bitcoin exchanges. For example, the fall of FTX destroyed eight billion in value. This has affected the price and confidence, but it was only a small percentage of the total market cap, and the system has withstood several earthquakes like this. More worrisome is the evidence that the FTX fraud was an active attack on Bitcoin using a con man who was a member of the psychopath club. This POST is the best summary of the grifters, pedophiles (yes), and bankruptcy as of the end of November 2022. From the article:

> The cast of characters... includes a mega-billionaire with enough influence to keep his life entirely off Wikipedia, a curious gathering of researchers at MIT, and also some familiar faces from the pandemic you might not have realized would pop up in the largest ever cryptocurrency catastrophe... Also Jeffrey Epstein... What I've gathered talking to people who have been around SBF (Sam Bankman Fried, the FTX CEO), superficially or closely... is that he's a spoiled, sadistic, hedonistic, ruthlessly dishonest bully of a manchild... [The plan was to:]
>
> Step 1: Establish Alameda Research trading firm.
>
> Step 2: Complete one kick-ass trade.
>
> Step 3: Build a well-projected media image of the Altruistic Death Star.
>
> Step 4: Build the Death Star (FTX-Alameda).
>
> Step 5: Explode.
>
> Sam Bankman Fried was pushing for more Bitcoin regulation in the weeks before the collapse of FTX (Epoch Times Nov 29, 2022). He has also admitted in an interview HERE that he was guilty of financial crimes.
>
> Analyst Lyn Alden comments:

"Seigniorage" is the profit that a government makes by issuing its own currency, especially as it relates to the difference between production cost (near zero) and its market value. Blockchain technology has enabled private entities to benefit from seigniorage as well. They can create a crypto semi-liquid/fungible asset for very little cost, hype it up, and try to profit from it. Because very little value is being created in the process, it's mostly a zero sum game where the creators and promoters of the coins make the money, and retail speculators lose the money.

All cryptocurrencies but Bitcoin are problematic, and Teather might prove a worse disaster than FTX. The 2nd Smartest Guy in the Room states, "A simple crypto rule to live by: any token or exchange that has a CEO, identifiable individual or development team associated with it is not real crypto; it's the antithesis of crypto. [I have] been warning for quite some time that all of these centralized exchanges are nothing more than grifting operations, IRS reporting nodes and CIA black ops money laundering facilitators." Peter McCormick calls all crypto but Bitcoin "s**tcoins."

Bitcoin transactions are slow. Applications like the Lightening Network are making Bitcoin faster, more scalable, and more accessible. Ms. Alden wrote a comprehensive article about this and its relationship to the currency HERE:

-Bitcoin started with a smart design from the beginning. It created an underlying digital gold and settlement network, with a credible degree of decentralization, auditability, scarcity, and immutability that no other network currently rivals. On top of that foundation, Lightning as a payment network is being developed, and has reached a critical mass of liquidity and usability.

-A truly decentralized and permissionless payment network [like Bitcoin] requires its own underlying self-custodial digital bearer asset. If instead it runs on top of the fiat currency system or relies on external custodial arrangements at its foundation, then it is neither decentralized nor permissionless.

-Many cryptocurrencies that followed in Bitcoin's wake put the cart before the horse. They optimized for throughput and speed on their base layer, at the cost of weaker decentralization, auditability, scarcity, and/or immutability of the underlying bearer asset. As such, they failed to gain structural adoption as money and rendered their high throughput irrelevant, especially since they were brought into existence in the shadow of Bitcoin's larger network effect.

-Volatility is inevitable along the path of monetization. A new money cannot go from zero to trillions without upward volatility by definition, and with upward volatility comes speculators, leverage, and periods of downward volatility. The first couple decades of monetization for the network as it undergoes open price discovery to reach the bulk of its total addressable market should be different than the "steady state" of the network after it reaches the bulk of its total addressable market, assuming it is successful in doing so.

-Taxes on cryptocurrency transactions, as well as the lower supply inflation rate of bitcoins compared to fiat currencies, results in Gresham's law being applicable here. Most people in developed countries have an incentive to spend their fiat and hoard their bitcoin like an investment, at least in this stage of the monetization process. The exception is for the subset of people who specifically need Bitcoin/Lightning's permissionless nature for one reason or another, or for whom the majority of their liquid net worth is in it.

-People in developing countries, with higher inflation and weaker payment and banking systems in general, have more of a natural incentive to use Lightning as a medium of exchange earlier on its monetization process. Indeed, adoption rates are rather promising in many of those regions. This isn't surprising, considering that more people in developing countries have smart phones than bank accounts, in aggregate.

Other resources

- For a comprehensive introduction, HERE is the complete two-day 2022 Pacific Bitcoin conference on YouTube. Some of it is insider baseball.
- From reader Tony Cecala: "The best way to learn about Bitcoin is to find local meetup groups of Bitcoin "maximalists." These people believe in the promise of Bitcoin to act as a hedge against inflation, censorship, and seizure of one's property. They say that money in an exchange is not your property, as you don't hold the "keys.""
- Listen to podcasts such as Peter McCormack's What Bitcoin Did.
- *The Bitcoin Standard: The Decentralized Alternative to Central Banking.*
- *Thank God for Bitcoin: The Creation, Corruption, and Redemption of Money.*
- *Bitcoin: Hard Money You Can't F*ck With: Why bitcoin will be the next global reserve currency.*

Bitcoin will do to banks what email did to the postal industry. —Rick Falkvinge

Part Twelve

Stay Frosty, Do Not Get Discouraged, and We Will Win

Chapter 50
Follow-up Letter to my Kids

I never sent this because they are still pissed about the last letter. One of them gave me a lecture that "all scientists agree" about carbon theories and global warming. He told me that I was spreading "misinformation."

* * *

I understand that rejecting parental advice is a universal feature of the late 20s age group--I went through it myself. I apologize for injecting myself into your business in the past and would not do it (outside of a few times when my judgment slipped) except for our mortal danger. You are in denial about current events.

Life seems normal in the USA, but totalitarianism is more blatant in other countries. Millions of people are rioting in Brazil, Chile has been locked down on and off, and there are miserable threats to Europe, including diesel shortages and nuclear war. Britain, Canada, Australia, and

Germany (and the US) are dominated by false governments that are dismantling freedoms.

The dollar is the most stable currency in history. When we lose the petrodollar and reserve currency status, our standard of living will crater. Will we soon be scrabbling after gold, Bitcoin, or (God forbid) a central bank digital theft-and-control currency? The censored media is covering all this up, so most of us are frogs in nearly boiling waters.

Your faulty assumption is that because America has not seen a population-wide genocide, it cannot be happening now. But it is. Watch THIS late 2022 video for the details. I get tearful when I view it. Black swan events are happening.

China is an opportunist rather than a prime mover, but they are at war with us. You may have yet to hear that 20 houses in [a subdivision where we own a vacation house] were recently bought by Chinese investors. This is personal if you know how China is attacking us in other ways.

Once again, I know how easy it is to dismiss parents because I did the same with mine. I decided about a year ago that I had to try to communicate with you because of the gravity of the situation. I knew then and understand now that it might burn our relationship to the ground. This was tremendously painful for me, but I had and have no other choice.

Blasting preconceptions is the hardest thing in life, but it is a survival skill when all our lives may soon be shredded. Everyone is out mowing their lawns instead of learning what is happening. I hate to lose contact with you, but what bothers me the most is that your ability to make judgments is compromised by propaganda.

All my love, —Robert

Chapter 51
Our Heroes Have Lashed Themselves to the Mast

Those who have the privilege to know have a duty to act.

— Albert Einstein

T he champions of the freedom movement persist through overwhelming difficulties and tolerate a cesspool of lawsuits, censorship, and defamation. They need your support.

* * *

Peter McCullough, MD, was the first to convince me that Covid and the vax were betrayals. He has been repeatedly attacked because of his work. For example, the American Board of Internal Medicine revoked his board certification. Since he is one of the most prominent living medical academics, with over 600 publications in peer-reviewed journals, this is like canceling a merit badge from his Boy Scout days. But it is being used to attack his finances, credibility, and hospital privileges.

375

Odysseus told his crew to tie him to the mast so he could listen to the Sirens without fear. Artist: Herbert James Draper

Worse, someone gave more than $30 million to plaintiffs' lawyers to harass him.* Even though McCullough is careful and his patient care immaculate, this kind of money requires an expensive legal defense. *Source: a friend who spoke to Dr. McCullough.

McCullough has been everywhere telling the truth. His Rogan interview #1747, HERE was his first influential work. If you, too, have benefitted from listening to him, support him HERE. I did.

Robert F. Kennedy, Jr., is a progressive insider and a member of the dominant 20th-century political family. He has had a storied and productive career; until recently, he was beloved by all. His Wikipedia entry says:

Cassandra's Memo

From 1986 until 2017, Kennedy was a senior attorney for the Natural Resources Defense Council (NRDC), a non-profit environmental organization. From 1984 until 2017, he was a board member and attorney for HudsonRiverkeeper.[4] Earlier in his legal career, he served as assistant district attorney in New York City. Kennedy was an adjunct environmental law professor at Pace University School of Law for over thirty years. Until August 2017, he held the post of supervising attorney and co-director of Pace Law School's Environmental Litigation Clinic, which he founded in 1987.

He was also part of a plaintiff's lawyer team who won a several billion-dollar judgment against Monsanto. (purchased by Bayer.) A jury found that their product glyphosate (Roundup) causes cancer. This story is ongoing.

Wikipedia and other sources claim, "He has promoted the scientifically discredited idea that vaccines cause autism."

Kennedy said in a Twitter post, "Our army is growing. Getting up and fighting for this is what you were put on this planet to do." He is throwing himself on a hand grenade to save us.

Like many others, he had a personal experience that taught him about vaccines. A flu shot damaged his voice, and he now has a syndrome called "spastic dysphonia." Click HERE to donate to Children's Health Defense. There is a California chapter as well.

Joseph Mercola, MD, is of a similar stature as RFK, Jr. Mercola is the *New York Times'* "number one misinformation spreader," which is a supreme endorsement. You can find his podcasts on Apple or Mercola's podcast website. You can subscribe to his blogs HERE. Once you understand his importance, you will never buy vitamins and supplements anywhere else.

Peter Breggin, MD, is known as the "conscience of psychiatry." For decades, he worked tirelessly to expose his corrupt specialty and its toxic medications. Since January 2020, with the advent of SARS-CoV-2, he and his wife Ginger have given most of their attention to the widespread frauds behind the Chinese virus pandemic. They emphasize the necessity of taking a determined political stand against the authoritarian and totalitarian intentions of those driving the attacks on our freedom. They wrote *COVID-19 and the Global Predators: We Are the Prey*, which has sold more than 200,000 copies. Go to Breggin.com to learn more and listen to their excellent podcast.

Steve Kirsch is the only Silicon Valley type who has publicly red-pilled and is actively fighting for our nation, healthcare, and constitution. Kirsch is abrasive and does not suffer fools. He says, "I have no conflicts of interest, and I cannot be intimidated. They cannot take away my license to practice medicine because I'm not a doctor. I'm worse. I'm an engineer with two degrees from MIT. And I have a lot of smart friends."

I read everything he writes. Subscribe to him, and you will have chances to help him as you learn. He is one of the major players in our war. To learn more, see HERE.

Naomi Wolf is a prolific feminist writer who identifies as a progressive. But like RFK Jr., she was thrown out and plastered with labels like "anti-vaxer." Her recently published book is *The Bodies of Others: The New Authoritarians, COVID-19, and The War Against the Human.* Her website is dailyclout.io. You can help her HERE.

Pierre Kory, MD, MPA, pulmonary and critical

care specialist, is the Front Line COVID-19 Critical Care Alliance (FLCCC) president. This group published COVID treatment protocols HERE. He led ICUs in multiple COVID-19 hotspots throughout the pandemic and co-authored five influential papers about the illness.

Paul Marik, MD, FCCM, FCCP is the cofounder of FLCCC and another huge contributor.

Simone Gold, MD, JD, started America's Frontline Doctors. When I first heard her speak, I thought, "With women like her on our side, how can we lose?" She was imprisoned for a few months for speaking at the January 6th rally at the Capital. HERE is her website, and HERE is how to donate to her group. Get on her mailing list.

Richard Fleming, JD, MD, Ph.D. is also part of the legal effort to lock up Fauci, Gates, and the rest. His website is flemingmethod.com, and you can help him by submitting letters to your state attorney general.

Vernon Coleman, MD, has been predicting current events for years. See vernoncoleman.org for his content. He writes:

> I was sued by all sorts of people [and]... I had MI5 and private detectives (hired by drug companies) chasing me and tracking me down. My mail was opened, and two separate insiders told me that Special Branch had a growing file about me... I was regularly filmed by police forces. I received writs so thick that they wouldn't fit through the letterbox and had to be pushed through a cat flap. I've had papers relating to drug companies stolen from my home. And, of course, my phone has been tapped for years.... (To continue, see HERE.)

Paul Alexander is a Trinidad-Canadian health researcher and a former Trump administration official at the US Department of Health and Human Services (HHS) during the pandemic. He inserted himself into and reported on Canadian and American trucker demonstrations. He has become a force on Substack and writes up to ten times daily. This is too much for some readers. Alexander does not hold back his feelings, which endears him to us. You can help him with a paid subscription HERE.

Catherine Austin Fitts originally freaked me out, but I now follow her like a Deadhead going to Grateful Dead concerts. Her Solari.com is for people who can either tolerate a conversion by blowtorch or already understand the basics.

Robert Malone did a seminal interview with Rogan (# 1757). But after Malone sued Peter Breggin and other freedom movement people, I have viewed him with skepticism. Breggin observed that Malone and a psychologist named Desmet blame the worldwide disasters on a psychological angst they label "mass formation psychosis." Breggin believes this takes responsibility away from the global predators. He is also concerned that the psychosis tag could mean that people concerned about events might be labelled crazy. In today's insane era, they might be given toxic psych medications.

Catherine Austin Fitz did a podcast that told the bottom line about these issues HERE. Her view was that Malone is sincere but has ridiculously thin skin, which should preclude his ambition to enter politics. See also THIS link on Breggin.com and my posts HERE, HERE, and Catherine Austin Fitts HERE. An exhaustive case against Malone is HERE or HERE. Look at it all and decide for yourself.

Malone's actions created a conflict that hurts our movement. Ginger and Peter Breggin are some of the most courageous and self-sacrificing people I have ever met. To help them with the lawsuit, please donate to their legal defense here: givesendgo.com/Breggin. I did.

These writers, speakers, activists, and podcasters deserve special mention. Some are anonymous, and many are on Substack: Lies are Unbekoming, CJ Hopkins, Igor's Newsletter, Toby Roger's Utopian, A Midwestern Doctor, James Roguski, Tess Lawrie, Patrick Moore, Tim and May Hindmarsh, Nick Yaya, Ronald Stein, Alex Epstein, David Carmichael, Silvia Cattori, Roberto Strongman, Vera Sharav, Tess Lawrie, Toby Rogers, 2nd Smartest Guy in the World, Christian Elliot, Abigail Shrier, Peter McCormack, Ryan Heath, Bryce Eddy, Frederick R. Smith Speaks, Scott Schara, Sherri Tenpenny, Jeff Childers, Exposing the Darkness.

One is a hero, and the other wears a yellow shirt.

Chapter 52
What Should You Do?

When a man knows he is to be hanged in a fortnight, it concentrates his mind wonderfully.

— Samuel Johnson

A reader wrote, "I just want to curl up in a ball and cover my ears." I feel the same way, but after I understood the stakes—western civilization itself —I had no choice but to act. This is not easy for me, either. My advice is to make preparations, learn quickly, and attach yourself to mentors. Then spread the word so that everyone will know the enemy.

* * *

My story

When your life is on the line, you think nothing of working hard. I discovered that I can still drink knowledge through a fire hose. I first researched our pathetic healthcare system and wrote about it in *Hormone*

Secrets and *Butchered by "Healthcare."* Then, over the last two years, I studied the disappointing current events in society and the world.

My vision has faded, and some of my skills may have waned, but I am still learning the equivalent of a master's degree a year. I have been writing, speaking, and studying eight or more hours daily, nearly seven days a week, for years. Thousands of awakened warriors around me are doing the same.

When I was an emergency doctor, I learned how to make decisions. The critical one was whether a patient went home or was admitted to the hospital. It is a simple binary, a switch to flip, but mistakes can be disastrous. We use foundational logic such as "cure-alls are dubious," "common things are more likely," and "one cause for a problem happens more often than many." The best of us refuse to be confused by arcane debates or academic absurdities. Our triage training allows us to process complex data rapidly.

* * *

Modeling is the most powerful way to grow and develop

Mentors are critical. Although I had a few from my prior authorship work, my first during my new period were Peter and Ginger Breggin.

RFK, Jr., is our most valuable guru. I am a distant acquaintance, so I asked him (or maybe heard on one of his podcasts) how he fought through the pressures. He said:

- He was trained in youth to believe there would be a time when he would be called on to make significant contributions.
- He faces the bad guys individually instead of considering the whole evil scene.
- He does not try to predict the future.

Being a plaintiff's attorney taught him patience. Their cases take many years to resolve.

Some of my other mentors are virtual, but I try to establish telephone and sometimes in-person contact with them. Dr. Joseph Mercola (Mercola.com), Paul Alexander, and many others are on Substack.com. Strangely, some listeners now regard me as a patriarch.

* * *

Preparations

The US is better insulated against food shortages than other countries—we produce 4,000 calories per person per day. Although most people need less than 2000, we force-feed ourselves an average of 2,750 with marketing. After learning this, if you are still worried about going hungry, you can store rice, beans, dried corn, whey protein powder, and canned animal fat (lard and ghee). This costs only a few hundred dollars for enough to last a year. Use 20-gallon plastic screw-top buckets purchased from pet stores or online sources.

Since red states protect citizens best, some people are considering moving. Florida is the obvious choice. But if you do not help with the fight, you might be decamping to the last part of the Titanic to slip under the waves.

After inflation impoverishes those on fixed incomes,

crime will escalate, so buy guns and learn how to use them. These are primarily for urban self-protection and may not be necessary if you do not live in a Democrat-led high-crime city. Do not completely discount the chance we will need them to defend our republic.

SUBSTACK LINK

My fuel is anger and love for my children.
The global predators have stolen so much from me. Some of my dear friends have died from the "vaccine," and others have mutated into wretched Covidian zombies. I cannot imagine how Scott Schara, Robb Garmong, and David Carmichael have suffered or how they feel after losing their loved ones. Thinking about the fertility disaster or the deaths and diseases the vax is causing is excruciating.

* * *

What about fear?
I know my life expectancy is short, and this somehow gives me courage. I also know that anyone expecting their path to be smooth and painless will be crushingly disap-

pointed. The only treatment for being overwhelmed is to grow and develop.

I sometimes think about this passage from Richard Morgan's novel *Thirteen*:

> If you work at it, you can reach a balance. The fear tips over into exhilaration. The weakness turns into strength. Fuels you up to face whatever it is your survival anxiety thinks it's warning you about. Starts to feel good instead of bad. Kind of addictive after a while.

And this quote from *Sacred Games*, an Indian novel about a mobster:

> I won't tell you that there was no fear in me, but I had learnt to bury it, to layer it over with thick sheets of indifference. Ever since that bullet had hurled into me, I knew how real death was. I had no illusions. I had seen that a woman can be alive one day, eating mutton and sneering and joking and thrusting out her chest, her eyes humming with laughter and hunger, and then the next day can find her unconscious in a hospital bed, her mouth open and gasping. I knew I was going to die, I was going to be killed. There was no escape for me. I had no future, no life, no retirement, no easy old age. To imagine any of that was cowardice. A bullet would find me first. But I would live like a king. I would fight this life, this bitch that sentences us to death, and I would eat her up, consume her every minute of every day. So I walked my streets like a lord of mankind, flanked by my boys.

* * *

What we must do

Individual civil liberties are our doctrine, not collectivist drivel about "the most good for the most people." If most of us understood this, ruinous vaccines designed to prevent hypothetical future bioweapon attacks would never be considered. Openness—free speech—is the first American value. "Security clearances" and government secrecy are contrary to this. Censorship is the worst, for if truth prevailed, our catastrophe would vanish.

Although we face wealthy, patient foes who are getting away with murder, they are not unbeatable. There are only a few thousand of them and billions of us. As a group, we are far more dangerous than the psychopaths. They are hindered by fatal hubris, swallow transparent frauds, and believe collectivist ideas that have been tried and failed countless times. There is no Great and Powerful Oz behind the curtain. They are small, aging, terrified men holding up a soggy tissue of transhumanist delusions to shield themselves from death.

If you hide now, you and your children will have an agonizing time later, for giving ground to predators emboldens them. If you think this is a spectator sport and do not help work the courts and the legislatures, civil disobedience will soon be all we have left. This is ugly and dangerous. The Chinese, with their sadistic rulers, are at this point now.

We will survive and even thrive if we step up. You have gotten my memo, and you must share it. Stay frosty, keep at it, and the calamity will go no further.

* * *

Optimism

- Our tattered US Constitution still lives, and there is good news from the US and Indian courts.
- I see daily proof of the seemingly infinite well of American strength, expertise, integrity, and advancements. I also know that the law of supply and demand trumps all the billionaires in the world.
- The majority of those playing along with the agendas seem to be acting. They retain their core values, self-interest, and primary focus on their families. The propaganda and cultural destruction they face are hard to ignore, but ignore it, they do. Immigrants are many of our best and may be our future leaders. They understand America's hope better than we do.
- With luck and resolve, our crises will force everyone to learn what has been done to them. If this were an age of reason, we would chop the conspirators' heads off and spike them on our nation's gates—and Gates, you would be first. But our future is less certain because we are infested by pandemics of narcissism, personal weakness, and absurd lies perpetrated by criminals.
- Children's Health Defense is sponsoring many legal actions; see HERE. They deserve your support.
- Reiner Fuellmich, the lawyer who took down Volkswagen for corrupt practices, says the US and Indian courts offer the most hope, and he is not quitting.

Cassandra's Memo

- THIS post by the anonymous "John Carter" is also optimistic. I am a fanboy of his writing, and I hope these visions are our future.
- Here is the conclusion of Paul Kingsnorth's book, *The Vaccine Moment* (2022):

The world is not a mechanism: it is a mystery, one that we participate in daily. When we try to redesign it like a global CEO, or explain it like an essayist, we are going to fail: weakly or gloriously, but fail we shall. The Machine, the technium, the metaverse: whatever we name our 21st century Babel, and however overwhelming it seems to us in the moment, it can never conquer in the end, because it is a manifestation of human will and not the will of God. If you don't believe in the will of God, call it the law of nature instead: either way, it speaks the same thing to us. It says, gently or firmly: *you are not in charge.*

I can't pretend to understand all of this. All I have is my intuition, and these words. But I think that the world is more surprising, and more alive, than I sometimes see or even want to believe. I think that the corona moment highlights an ancient ongoing struggle, between the spirit of the wild and the spirit of the Machine, and that this struggle goes on around us and inside us all every minute of the day.

Sometimes, battles must be fought, stands taken, lines drawn. This is one of those times. Once we begin to understand all the stories at play, we can begin to see which one we are taking part in, and what choices we must make: what we stand for, and what we will not. If we refuse the future that is being laid out before us - if we refuse the Machine - we do not have the choice, at this moment in history, to sit in silence.

Robert Yoho, MD (ret)

The times demand now that we remember and culti-
vate some of the old virtues. We could start with courage:
courage and patience. It may take years, decades,
centuries, but the Machine we have built to manage life
itself, to squeeze the world into our own small shape - it
will come down in the end, and the humming wires will
fall silent. Our task in the meantime is to understand, so
that we can resist, the shape of the tyranny it brings.

But D. H. Lawrence knew: all the prophets knew.
The Earth cannot be reset. Not by us; not ever.

They talk of the triumph of the machine,

but the machine will never triumph.

Out of the thousands and thousands of centuries
of man

the unrolling of ferns, white tongues of the acanthus
lapping at the sun, for one sad century

machines have triumphed, rolled us hither and
thither,

shaking the lark's nest till the eggs have broken.

Shaken the marshes, till the geese have gone

and the wild swans flown away singing the swan-
song at us.

Hard, hard on the earth the machines are rolling,

but through some hearts they will never roll.

Chapter 53
Diversion: Even Hobbits Have a Part to Play

Frodo: *I wish the Ring had never come to me. I wish none of this had happened.*

Gandalf: *So do all who live to see such times, but that is not for them to decide. All we have to decide is what to do with the time that is given to us.*

— J.R.R. Tolkien, The Lord of the Rings

Tolkien, Orwell, and many others wrote about periods of human suffering, and our grandparents lived through them. Ours is not a unique or novel situation for history or literature--we face ancient evils. Once we understand this, we must act as our forefathers did —with courage, sacrifice, and resolution.

Near the end of Tolkien's *Lord of the Rings* is a chapter describing how the Hobbits returned to their homeland and found a disaster that mirrors today's:

Robert Yoho, MD (ret)

The land looked rather sad and forlorn... [and there was] an unusual amount of burning going on, and smoke rose from many points round about...

Psychopaths had grabbed power and were stealing from everyone. There were new laws, free speech was gone, and businesses were closed:

> On every wall, there was a notice and a list of Rules...
> The leader of the Shirriffs, a two-feather hobbit [said] 'You're arrested for Gate-breaking, Tearing up of Rules, and Assaulting Gate-keepers, Trespassing, and Sleeping in Shire-buildings without Leave, and Bribing Guards with Food.'

The Shire had its politicians, billionaires, corruption, and even a bogus leader.

> 'It all began with Pimple, as we call him,' said Farmer Cotton; 'and it began as soon as you'd gone off, Mr. Frodo. He'd funny ideas had Pimple. Seems he wanted to own everything himself, and then order other folk about. It soon came out that he already did own a sight more than was good for him; and he was always grabbing more, though where he got the money was a mystery: mills and malt-houses and inns, and farms, and leaf-plantations. He'd already bought Sandyman's mill before he came to Bag End, seemingly.

So the hobbits "raised the Shire:"

> 'Now! Wake all our people! They hate all this, you can see: all of them except perhaps one or two rascals and a

few fools that want to be important, but don't at all understand what is really going on. *But Shire-folk have been so comfortable so long they don't know what to do* (my emphasis). They just want a match, though, and they'll go up in fire. The Chief's Men must know that. They'll try to stamp on us and put us out quick. We've only got a very short time.

Although Tolkien denied it, his critics thought this chapter was a metaphor for Britain after World War II. His description of the lies, suppression of dissent, and selling totalitarianism using failed socialist ideas look similar to today.

We are now close to war. We have billions injured, many millions dead, and millions more still being murdered by the vax and withheld Covid therapies. Totalitarian controls starved and damaged others. All this is being done to gather wealth, power, and control into the hands of a few. What is happening is ancient, recurrent, and even Biblical. No novelist or historian should be surprised.

Our tale is still being written, and we must continue to battle monsters. Since there are many more of us than them, we will prevail if we rise to the occasion.

Awake! Awake! Fear, Fire, Foes.

Robert Yoho, MD (ret)

Awake! Fire, Foes! Awake!

SUBSTACK LINK

Part Thirteen
Bonus Section One

Chapter 54
TMI About Psychopaths

Psychology and characteristics
Psychopaths have high rates of violence. In one study, two-thirds of their victims were male strangers selected for retribution or a predatory purpose. Purposeful violence is less common for non-psychopaths. They mostly commit crimes of passion against female family members or acquaintances.

Only about a tenth of psychopaths are female.

A psychopath can perpetrate any violation of the rights of others or any evil deed and still sleep at night because he believes he is always right. And since these people do not think their behavior is wrong, they never seek treatment. They will participate in therapy programs to gain release from prison. There is no cure for them, however.

Debates with sociopaths are useless. No matter what we say or how much evidence is given, it has no meaning to them. Their sole goal is to fool us into classifying them as normal, so they can continue to use, deceive, and control us.

Even those who are armored with skepticism should never underestimate their chances of being fooled by the next psychopath. These degenerates do not display anxiety, remorse, or any feelings about others that would reveal them. Many, however, are practiced at feigning these human qualities.

Examples of psychopathic behavior from Łobaczewski and others

- A mother plays a game of hide and seek with her four-year-old daughter. She is holding a large kitchen knife. She tells her daughter, "I am going to count to one hundred, and if I find you, I will cut off your thumbs." The girl hides in her closet, and the mother, knowing where she is, lets her stay there, terrified, frightened, and traumatized until the last moment. When the mother opens the door, she cuts the skin under one of her daughter's thumbs.
- A family has two sons. One of them commits suicide using a hunting rifle. At Christmas, the parents give the gun to their other son. When asked why, they respond, "It was a perfectly good gun."
- Hare reports about psychopaths abusing the elderly. For example, after a criminal cons an older woman out of her life savings, a colluding psychopath contacts the victim. He claims to be a lawyer and offers to get the money back for a fee. The victim borrows the payment from a relative and loses it to the second criminal.
- Using lawsuits, rich people sometimes sue middle-class people to force them to pay ruinous lawyers' fees. These expenses are like buying paperclips for the wealthy, and winning

or losing—or even the issues litigated—are typically unimportant to them. Here is one example, and the others are legion. Some New York apartment co-ops are inhabited by people worth tens of millions. But if they allow the wrong billionaire into their midst, he can dominate them with litigation threats. The co-op admission committees typically ask for twenty (20) references, then turn many people down anyway.

- I knew a wealthy doctor who sued patients, and patients sued him. He also sued tenants, suppliers, and even moving companies. Some of his tenants won countersuits. One of his patients sued him for malpractice, lost the countersuit, and spent ten years trying to get the judgment overturned. By the time everyone finally walked away, the court had seized her house. After it was sold, no money was left for the doctor after the loan, realtors, and bankruptcy trustee were paid. This woman's total lawyer bills were $500,000. The doctor must have enjoyed it all because it was not profitable. I was informally sympathetic to this woman, so he called and threatened me. On another occasion, he tried to get me thrown out of our professional organization, and I had to defend myself in front of a committee. They told us to stay away from each other, which was wise advice. I was (more) abrasive in those days.

- **When corporate leaders are psychopaths**

Companies are indifferent to right or wrong. They do not care about human harm except as it impacts their core value, profit. Although corporate structures are not inherently sadistic or destructive, they can be led this way by their executives. When this happens, the corporations they control turn evil.

Nonprofits are subject to less oversight than for-profit corporations because, under some circumstances, they have no board of directors. They are not constrained by a requirement to make money, either.

Corporations have attained many legal aspects of personhood, which is problematic for their regulation. They are also potentially immortal. This means they can accumulate wealth over generations without the tax consequences that happen to the estates of individuals at their death. Over the past few decades, companies have skirted election donation laws and given massive amounts to politicians who can help them. And many corporations are now transnational, which makes controlling and punishing them difficult.

Łobaczewski says that psychopaths are incapable of creative work

They must depend upon ordinary people for this. As long as core parts of an economy still function, their pathological strategies may seem successful. However, a downward spiral begins when significant positions of power in business, government, and industry are filled with these people. Societies fail as they become colonized.

Ordinary people eventually recognize what their leaders are and devise survival strategies. But when a society comes to its senses, other deviants typically step in. These are often the same people. For example, at the fall of Soviet communism, capitalist psychopaths took the spoils, and many communists found a comfortable new home.

In their dealings with these criminals, people from the former Soviet block have advantages over Westerners. Soviet people have been under the regimes for so long that they routinely ignore rhetoric from the media, government, and corporations. They develop the ability to read between the propaganda lines (lies) and speculate about the truth. They can also spot people who pretend to be revolutionaries but are rats for the state. They regard Americans as easily fooled.

> I was a loyal Soviet citizen until the age of 20. What it meant to be a loyal citizen was to say what you were supposed to say, to read what you're permitted to read, to vote the way you were told to vote and, at the same time, to know that it was all a lie
>
> — Natan Sharansky, from a prison cell

The ability to cheat, lie, and kill with indifference is a stupendously successful adaptation. It has widened the gap between the middle class and the extremely wealthy. Advances in communication and propaganda technology have enabled these mutants to attempt a worldwide coup. As they gain more power, little restrains them. Psychopaths like Gates, whose true natures were hidden, are revealing themselves.

Counterpoint by Substack author A Midwestern Doctor

While I agree that things look bleak, the silver lining is that at least a third of the populace is waking up to the criminality and the agendas. For example, distrust of the Covid vaccine is being carried over to the other childhood vaccines. This will be a huge financial loss for Pharma.

About terminology

In psychiatry, the terms psychopath, sociopath, border-line personality, and anti-social personality are used as near-synonyms. Their verbiage changes kaleidoscopically and reflects the politically correct message *du jour*. I will not dignify the field's contribution by calling any of these diagnoses.

"Psychosis" refers to people who have trouble determining what is real and what is not. Auditory hallucinations are more typical for "schizophrenia," which is a wastebasket diagnosis encompassing related syndromes. Visual hallucinations are more likely when the psychosis is drug-induced. Psychopaths may seem psychotic to ordinary people, but they are not.

Yoho notes

- I have focussed on Łobaczewski's description of the extreme end of the spectrum, but he describes many cases as "subclinical."
- The lesser variants feel some pain and guilt, bond with certain people, and may have little idea that they are different.
- I have observed that those with psychopathic features may have trouble identifying others like them. This could be because lies and unethical actions seem reasonable to them. This weakness allows these degenerates to take advantage of each other.
- Sophisticated "normals" may be able to identify psychopaths more easily than the psychopaths themselves.

- A close friend with a few of these features understood global events early. He told me, "They want to kill us."

Popular books and articles

Snakes in Suits, when psychopaths go to work (2006) by Robert Hare and Paul Babiak

Without Conscience (1993) by Robert Hare

The Sociopath Next Door (2006) by Martha Stout

The Psychopath Test (2011) by Jon Ronson is a humorous account that points out inconsistencies but trivializes his subject.

More technical works

The Mask of Sanity (1941) by Dr. Hervey Cleckley. Brilliant case reports

Political Ponerology, A science on the nature of evil adjusted for political purposes (1984), by Andrzej Łobaczewski. Huge, comprehensive, and still relevant. See the interview with the editor, Chapter 3.

Related

HERE and HERE are overviews of the depopulation agenda.

A reader comments about the banality of evil, "Fauci and Brix with her scarves seemed so ordinary. Gates, too, seems so banal. Terrible speaker. Boring."

Chapter 55
Digression: How I Wrote Three Ph.D. Theses in Six Years

The most important things are the hardest to say. They are the things you get ashamed of...

— Stephen King

I published four books on Amazon and 200,000 words on Substack, but no one gave me diplomas. Since physicians are not trained writers, I read, studied, and practiced to learn the trade. As I improved, other writing began to look less refined, so I wrote this essay to explain my new skills. If you do not write seriously, you may think I am a nitpicker. Those who are advanced may find these ideas elementary or confining.

If your writing is not outstanding, people will ignore you no matter how good your ideas are. *If you are ignored, you are writing a diary.*

SUBSTACK LINK

Cassandra's Memo

* * *

Basics

- Stephen King wrote, "If you want to be a writer, you must do two things above all others: read a lot and write a lot."
- Your sole goal is to shepherd your readers through your material. It is not about you, so never show off. Avoid fancy words and simplify. This is a lot of effort.
- Hemingway wrote, "The first draft of anything is shit." Excellence, inspiration, and even greatness may emerge if you rewrite enough. This is the only path to competence unless you are a genius. It is freakily time-consuming but satisfying if you have the "bug."
- If you are a beginner, you can still do competent work if you spend enough time editing.
- Nathaniel Hawthorne wrote, "Easy reading is damn hard writing." Perfection can require fifty drafts, but if you have been studying and thinking about a subject for years, you might need fewer.

- Faulkner said writers must "kill all your darlings." This means cutting and burning any part of your work that does not fit perfectly with the rest, no matter how much you like it.
- As your skills improve, it all requires less effort.
- You must have both foundational knowledge of your subject and enough life experience to interpret it.
- All writing and all thoughts should be condensed into chunks of between 1000 and 2500 words. This is the ideal chapter or essay length. Much more, and you lose most people. Your word processor will tell you where you are. Note: a subset of nonfiction blog readers crave longer analyses of 10,000 words or more. A Midwestern Doctor does this successfully on Substack.
- Long, awkward posts with sound ideas can be trimmed into excellence with enough effort. Some recommend racing through your first draft and then editing, but this is not my approach.
- Mentors are vital. You must get all the help you can from friends, editors, and family. Pay professionals if you have the resources. College writing professors say that their best students need little help, and their worst ones are beyond help. Most of us are somewhere in between.
- Use your thesaurus constantly. Tip: if you have a complex, descriptive word, look for one that is more commonly used but still appropriate. I prefer powerthesaurus.org.

- The structure is everything. Your reader must flow from one point to another. If you make them stumble, they will leave. To get it right, rearrange words in the sentences, sentences in the paragraphs, and the paragraphs themselves.
- Revise your title and internal topic headings over and over until they are perfect. For a final polish, read the document aloud.
- George Orwell wrote, "Writing a book is a horrible, exhausting struggle, like a long bout with some painful illness. One would never undertake such a thing if one were not driven on by some demon whom one can neither resist nor understand."

Style

Read George Orwell's essay, Politics and the English Language, monthly until it is cemented into your thinking. Here is part of it:

i.   Never use a metaphor, simile, or another figure of speech that you are used to seeing in print.

ii.   Never use a long word where a short one will do.

iii.   If it is possible to cut a word out, always cut it out.

iv.   Never use the passive where you can use the active.

v.   Never use a foreign phrase, a scientific word, or a jargon word if you can think of an everyday English equivalent.

vi. Break any of these rules sooner than say anything outright barbarous.

Grammar and usage errors cause readers to pause and some to quit. Learn how to weed these out. Review punctuation until it is part of your hard drive. Here are a few tips:

- Dashes are used for emphasis or drama. Do not overdo it.
- "Which" is used when separating clauses and requires a comma. "That" does not.
- Combining related complete sentences using commas sometimes works. Dependent clauses at the beginning of sentences require commas, while those at the end do not.
- Be consistent—either use or avoid contractions. For example, do not mix "don't" with "do not" in the same document.
- Commas should separate two adjectives that are side-by-side and modify the same noun.
- Lists separated by commas must include a comma after the next-to-last item.
- Typos invariably creep into even heavily edited final manuscripts. A proofreader should correct these if you want your work to rise to the near perfection of a book.

You should check your writing by copying and pasting each chapter into a website that measures the grade level, such as readabilityformulas.com. The lower the level, the easier the essay is to read. My first book was at the 11th-grade level, and my second, written after more practice, was at the 9th. This chapter, and much of *Cassandra's Memo*, is at the 7th.

A reader commented, "I prefer not to read at a 7th-grade level, thank you!"

I replied: "Good point. *The Real Anthony Fauci* is 12th-grade reading, and I enjoy RFK's prose." Writing like this lends color and yields insights into the author's sophistication. Some of the people I excerpted are also at higher levels. (But some of their work could be more tightly edited.)

Writing at lower grade levels is not condescending. Writers use every possible trick to drag readers through the ideas, and if I used $50 words, it would delay comprehension for many and stop some of the less motivated. The other bonus is that advanced readers with extensive skills can rapidly scan lower-grade-level prose.

Other key tips

- Paragraphs should be five sentences or less. This is a firm but not an absolute rule. Sometimes one sentence works.
- Steven King wrote, "The road to hell is paved with adverbs." Delete them! Example: *extremely* improbable." Make your sentences declarative and straightforward.
- Full-time writers use parentheses and semicolons every other week—or never. Write around them. And as F. Scott Fitzgerald wrote, "An exclamation point is like laughing at your own joke."

- Never hit the return twice at the end of paragraphs. Modern word-processing programs require only one return.
- Your online blog post may contain some individual style, but do not overdo it. I use bold font at the start of a few related paragraphs. Books should be more traditional.
- Your messages must speak for themselves. Avoid internal comments such as "interestingly," "quite noteworthy," "it should be noted," or "this deserves mentioning."
- Authors who read great fiction improve their skills. Some reread their favorites many times. Hunter S. Thompson hand-copied Dickens' books, for example.
- ALL CAPS is a rookie's mistake, of which I am sometimes guilty. YOU SELDOM WANT TO SHOUT. If you use a web or blog style, bold or italics headings are easier on the eyes.
- The sentence structure should be as short as possible without overdoing it. Cut them up! An occasional longer, more complex sentence may help the flow. Your writing program will tutor you. I have used the paid version of Grammarly for years. Some of my friends use Hemmingwayapp.com.
- Never reference your point of view by writing words such as "I thought," "It seemed to me," "I found," or "I came across." The reader already knows that you are the author.
- Learn about the passive voice from programs such as Grammarly. Passive has its uses for nonfiction writers, who should not try to abolish

it altogether. Fiction writers should drive a stake through its heart. The free version of Grammarly found 16 errors in the first draft of this essay. The paid version teaches you more.

Other programs

I firmly recommend that you use Scrivener for writing books. It has a superb autocorrect function and simplifies many other tasks, including moving chapters around and searching the entire manuscript. It automatically backs up to your hard drive at intervals. If you do not use it, you will waste a quarter of your time.

Having MS Word on your computer is helpful but costly. You should also be familiar with Google Docs. Use this to publish individual essays on the internet for free. These have their own "URL" web locations, so you can use them as reference links. Dropbox has the same feature if you are getting away from the Google platform.

This is the fourth book I have self-published on Amazon and other platforms. I wrote most of these in Scrivener. I then used Vellum to typeset them, which creates a MS Word version, and transferred the files to Amazon's Kindle Direct Publishing (KDP). If you get the formatting details right in your source document, you will not have to correct errors later. Chief among these is to use a single space between paragraphs.

I composed my titles and planned the covers myself. I directed contractors from Upwork to make the art according to my specifications, and they supplied flair and some colors. This took months.

The reward for developing all these skills is that you can change anything in a few hours. You need not wait for an expensive contractor—even after your book is published.

Fonts

Some writers spend lifetimes obsessing over these. I spent a week reading about them. You can go as deep as you want or take my advice and use Georgia or another modern "serif" typeface that has small appendages on each letter. Georgia is free and works well for both print and computer. "Sans serif" fonts without appendages are popular for computers and web publishing, but this is a personal choice. Be considerate—your type size should be large enough that older people can easily read it.

Backup and censorship

I copy and back up each Substack post into a Scrivener document as a chapter. Unlike many word processing programs, this works well for text, formatting, and images. If you decide to write a book later, your posts will be on a program that allows convenient editing, organization, and manipulation.

I copy my desktop at intervals onto a hard drive. Apple, Google, or Dropbox cloud backup is another good idea. Research the tradeoffs between these, including the potential for censorship and deplatforming.

I always copy and preserve each post's original web address (URL). In the worst circumstance, my computer and backups could be stolen or lost. Substack might go down, be bought, or get censored. But if I have those URLs (keep them secret, keep them safe!), I can still recover my content using the Wayback Machine Internet Archive. Nothing ever dies on the internet as long as this is alive and well. Given current trends, there is cause for concern about this.

You can also direct the Wayback Archive to save your posts under a new URL as you finish each one. This might be more secure. If you preserve your content, you live to fight another day.

If Substack goes down, savvy authors with backups can immediately move to the next platform. Bastyon.com might be a good choice because it is rumored to be censor-proof.

Inspiration

Your age, intellect, and experiences dictate what material is credible for your writing ambitions. For example, older people can opine about youth, but the reverse is tricky. Another example: current events seen through the lens of Chris Bray, an American history academic, yield insights. A third: Grant Horner is a Christian academic and a Milton scholar who often has a fresh take on complex matters. My outlook on today's events combines my recent research, medical background, and the medical corruption material.

You must be comfortable writing through your own eyes. This odd-sounding advice means you must explain your truths even if it feels like a privacy invasion. This is necessary to get the best out of yourself. If you have never been afraid to push the "publish" button, you have yet to write your best work.

Narration and podcasting

Substack and other platforms allow you to narrate your posts. Most people find that this comes to them faster than writing skills. Rather than dictating into your platform's recorder, use a program on your computer, such as Garageband for Mac, then upload the result. That way, you keep a backup. Your voice clarity will improve with practice and serve you well on podcasts.

Go on as many podcasts as you can to promote your content. Pitch these at matchmaker.fm, which costs $100 a year. Other sites that hook you up are more expensive. Let me know if you find any others that you like.

Be courteous and helpful to beginning podcasters. Two of my hosts were only fifteen years old. Accept offers to speak on small platforms—it is good karma, and they sometimes refer you to big ones.

Doing your own podcast on Substack, Buzzsprout, or other programs requires another modest learning curve. These use an "RSS feed" that puts your content on Apple Podcast and many other platforms. With few exceptions (boycott Spotify!), these are uncensored. A good microphone and video camera are $180, and the support websites are about $20 a month. You can also post on Rumble, Bitchute, or others for free. YouTube has turned traitor and actively censors.

You are committing to sitting in front of a computer all day

Learn about electric and magnetic fields (EMFs). These are short wavelength radiation from WiFi, microwaves, and cell towers. Take simple steps to moderate your exposure. You should:

Turn your cell phone to airplane mode as much as you can.

Use your phone solely on the speaker and keep it away from your ears. The small print warnings for your device recommend this because highly suggestive evidence relates EMF to brain tumors.

Turn off your home's WiFi at night.

Stay away from your microwave oven when it is in use, or replace it with a convection oven.

Some disconnect their WiFi altogether and hardwire their TVs and computers to Ethernet. This older technology works faster but is less convenient.

Read about the dangers of EMF exposure. These hazards are taken far more seriously in Europe than in the

US. The Children's Health Defense website is a good source. Books include *Disconnect* by Devra Davis and *Dirty Electricity* by Samuel Milham.

On a related subject, blue light exposure from computers, TVs, and other screens can be detrimental as well, interfering with sleep cycles and causing vision decline. The simple way to mitigate this is to wear glasses that filter for it. These may be either amber or clear.

Indispensable* for book self-publishing and marketing

Kindlepreneur.com*

Vellum* typesetting program

Scrivener* writing program

Your book cover, title, and blurb must be perfect, or your book will sell poorly. Learn about these, then spend weeks perfecting yours. HERE is an excellent article about how to write a great blurb.

Amazon Ads* is powerful. This is a paid but sometimes censored search engine. They refuse books about treatments that compete with big Pharma's drugs, such as *Hormone Secrets*. I use Michal Stawicki (resurrectingbooks.com) for Ads. I found him on kindlepreneur.com. He has placed hundreds of thousands of keywords for me for *Butchered*, and he gets half the profits.

If you manage to make money, you are an exceptional animal. After over five years of full-time effort, my earnings are less than $300 a month. This includes my books, which are on both Amazon and other markets. I also get a small income from Substack. I might have done better had I focused more on money, but I was more interested in spreading my messages.

Fiction is sometimes profitable. Successful authors

usually write a lot—sometimes a hundred thousand words every month or two.

Where am I in this writing fraternity? I am a popularizer with podcasting skills trying to communicate basics. I have been told I have a smooth radio voice. I must spend untold hours editing.

Ideas from the photo above

I recommend Cultured Code Things* personal organizer (left) if you do not have another like OmniFocus. Things has cloud backup that transfers notes between all networked devices. Unfortunately, as my lists grow, like the Hotel California, some of the guests never check out!

The Scrivener* file above is a backup for most of my Substack articles. I still use Gmail but am switching to Proton mail. I do final editing on Substack.* My computer is wired for Ethernet.

Sources include

Stephen King: *On Writing*

Steven Pressfield: *Do the Work, The War of Art, Turning Pro*

John McPhee: *Draft no. 4 On the Writing Process*

I'm not fond of most writing podcasts. The ones for book marketing include Dave Chesson* at kindlepre neur.com*, and Mark Dawson's Self-Publishing Show.

Part Fourteen

Bonus Section Two: Podcasts

Chapter 56
RFK, Jr., Exposes Fauci, Gates, and AIDS

To understand *The Real Anthony Fauci*, you must read Dr. Yoho's *Butchered by Healthcare*.

— PB, a reader

TONY LYONS, THE CEO of Skyhorse Publishing, and editor Sofia Karstens speak about The Real Anthony Fauci.

Mr. Lyons has published hundreds of books and specializes in controversial subjects that traditional publishers avoid. To make sure that RFK's messages were heard, he cut the ebook's price to $3. This must have cost him millions.Sofia is a brilliant Kennedy insider who worked with their team to be sure the book was accurately referenced and edited. Gavin de Becker, the author of *The Gift of Fear*, also helped.

RFK, Jr. is a polymath who towers over his detractors, the media, and even the people surrounding him. I asked him how he managed to put his book together in eight months, and he modestly replied that he had book-writing experience from his other work. He confirmed that he hand-wrote the entire thing.

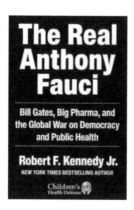

I gave *The Real Anthony Fauci* ebook or hard cover to over 100 of my friends and supporters. When you read it, you will learn why. It has over 18,000 five-star Amazon reviews and has sold over a million copies. It was the number-one worldwide nonfiction bestseller for months, even though the *New York Times* never reviewed it and has not acknowledged its success with the number-one best-seller status.

While reviewing *The Real Anthony Fauci* for the inter-view, I was once again struck by the profound criminality of Fauci, Gates, the research doctors, and the Pharma compa-nies. Lives lost are no obstacle for these people. Fauci works from a playbook that dates from the AIDS/AZT days. His motto must be that you can sell anything—even fraudulent, harmful drugs like the clot shot and AZT. His habit of lying about nearly everything is a psychopathic trait.

Since Gates is a eugenicist, killing people is his obses-sion. If you study him, you will see Asperger's syndrome monomania.

Cassandra's Memo

SUBSTACK LINK

I have wondered why these conspirators did not completely fabricate their studies and use saline injections. They get away with almost any other fakery, and this would have prevented deaths. But since Gates' goal is "population control," which means genocide, deaths were a feature of his plans, not a bug. In a TED talk, he famously spoke about reducing the world's people by ten percent. He is the founder of "The Bill and Melinda Gates Foundation for Population Control."

HERE is the Amazon link to buy the book. The Kindle version remains at $3 for now. Kennedy has his excellent podcasts HERE. Most are under half an hour, and I run them at double speed.

* * *

THE "GERM GAMES" pandemic simulations preceded Covid

These were confessions of crimes before they were committed. Kennedy tells about several of these in *The Real Anthony Fauci*, Chapter 12.

Robert Yoho, MD (ret)

SUBSTACK LINK

Excerpt:

Dark Winter, Atlantic Storm, and Global Mercury were only three of over a dozen Germ Games staged by military, medical, and intelligence planners leading up to COVID-19. Each of these Kafkaesque exercises became uncanny predictors of a dystopian age that pandemic planners dubbed the "New Normal." The consistent feature is an affinity among their simulation designers for militarizing medicine and introducing centralized autocratic governance.

SPARS-2017 was one of these games... The exercise turned out to be an eerily precise predictor of the COVID-19 pandemic exactly three years later.

According to the scenario, by late January, SPARS has spread to every state and forty-two countries. In record speed, a coalition of ingenious corporate and heroic government officials miraculously produce a new vaccine, "Corovax," just in time for a July 2026 Emergency Use Authorization rollout.

...Even a casual read of the Foundation's planning document makes clear that Gates's preparation has little to do with public health and everything to do with limiting freedom and aggressively marketing vaccines.

...The planners tell their intended audience—"public health providers and pandemic communicators"—that public concerns over worrisome reactions and vaccine side effects can be drowned out by flooding the airwaves with good news about vaccine successes. The dismaying role of mainstream media in these exercises is to broadcast propaganda, impose censorship, and manufacture consent for oppressive policies. In their projections, the social planners project absolute confidence that news media and social media companies will fully cooperate with this coup d'état. According to organizers, the purpose of Gates's simulation was to prepare "public health communicators" with a step-by-step strategic playbook for the upcoming pandemic. Eighteen months into the COVID-19 pandemic, it is difficult to peruse Gates's detailed 2018 planning document without feeling that we are all being played...

"These are brainwashing exercises," says former CIA officer and whistleblower Kevin Shipp. "Getting all of these thousands of public health and law enforcement officials to participate in blowing up the US Bill of Rights in these exercises, you basically have obtained their prior sign-off on torpedoing the Constitution to overthrow its democracy. They know that none of these participants are going to suddenly start soul-searching when the real thing happens. The CIA has spent decades studying exactly how to control large populations using these sorts of techniques." Shipp adds: "We are all subjects now being manipulated in a vast population-wide Milgram experiment, with Dr. Fauci playing the doctor in the white lab coat instructing us to ignore our virtues and our conscience and obliterate the Constitution."246

* * *

EVERYTHING I EVER LEARNED about AIDS was a pack of lies

No man ever steps in the same river twice, for it's not the same river, and he's not the same man.

— Heraclitus

The following story is unflattering to me. I spent my professional career ambling along, secure in my belief that the medical mythology I had memorized had integrity. But over the past few years, I have been proven wrong about many of my cherished illusions. A recent stunner was when I realized that what I had been taught about AIDS was false.

SUBSTACK LINK

I had my first chance to learn this several years ago when a brilliant friend and editor of Butchered by "Healthcare" said that the HIV theory of AIDS was fabricated and promoted along with the worthless, toxic AZT treatments (Thanks for everything, M!). Since I could not face another red pill after all the horrors I had uncovered, I ignored her.

RFK describes how the HIV virus link with AIDS is tenuous, how AZT treatments kill far more patients than they save, and how Fauci perpetrated these frauds to make money for industry and further his career.

The following is from Chapter 3, The HIV Pandemic Template for Pharma Profiteering.

> [Harvey Bialy says AIDS has] been a closed book for fifteen years. It has been clear for fifteen years that this is a non-infectious condition that has its cause in a whole variety of chemicals." His voice rises. "Doesn't the book demonstrate very clearly that scientifically, nothing happened between 1994 and 2003? Zero. Absolutely nothing except one wrong epidemiological prediction after another, one failed poisonous drug after another. 0.000.000 cured. No vaccine, or even a fake vaccine. It's a total failure. We've turned virology inside out and upside down to accommodate this bullshit hypothesis for seventeen years now. It's enough.
>
> — *Serious Adverse Events: An Uncensored History of AIDS,* by Celia Farber, quoted in *The Real Anthony Fauci*

...The AIDS pandemic proved a launch pad for Dr. Fauci's stellar rise. The lessons he learned from orchestrating regulatory responses to the AIDS crisis would become familiar templates for managing subsequent pandemics. Tony Fauci spent the next half-century crafting public responses to a series of real and concocted viral outbreaks[40,41]—HIV/AIDS[42] in 1983; SARS[43] in 2003; MERS[44,45,46] in 2014; bird flu[47,48] in 2005; swine flu ("novel H1N1")[49] in 2009; dengue[50,51] in 2012; Ebola[52] in 2014–2016; Zika[53] in 2015–2016; and COVID-19[54] in 2020.

Chapter 57
Dr. Mercola Interviews Finance Guru Edward Dowd

The desire to tell the truth is therefore only one condition for being an intellectual. The other is courage, readiness to carry on rational inquiry to wherever it may lead...

— Paul Baran

Edward Dowd and Dr. Joseph Mercola spoke in September 2022 about the coming financial collapse. Dowd was a former hedge fund and equity portfolio manager for BlackRock, one of the two largest asset companies in the world.

Note: I recorded this at 1.25 x speed. Many podcast and audiobook addicts listen at up to 2 x speed. This skill accelerates learning and is essential to avoid boredom. You may have better sound quality if you use the original platform.

SUBSTACK LINK

Robert Yoho, MD (ret)

Chapter 58
Alternative Medicine Sometimes Works Better than Mainstream

T estosterone treatment cures many cases of breast cancer and should be a standard practice. But although this is described in medical journals, it is hidden because hormones cannot be patented and do not make money for Pharma. I interviewed a patient whose tumor had spread to her bones—she was a stage 4, weighed under 100 pounds, and was using a walker. After starting treatment, within a few months, she gained 15 pounds. She emailed me from a beach in Mexico that she was still feminine and felt great despite using male doses of testosterone.

The following is from *Hormone Secrets*.

Can hormones be used to treat cancer? Yes. Testosterone suppresses breast cancer. Oral estradiol is safe and efficacious for treating prostate cancer. Patients using these hormones do not get damaging deficiency syndromes. Whether they work better than the industry's conventional therapies is unknown. Costly studies will never be done because human hormones can rarely be patented— they are unprofitable compared to patent drugs...

Rebecca Glaser, MD, published her successful experience treating breast cancer using implantable pellets combining testosterone and a blocker drug. She placed these under the skin close to the cancers. Charles Mok, DO, shrank a woman's breast cancer by 75 percent in six months using testosterone pellets (personal communication. He wrote Testosterone, Strong Enough for a Man, Made for a Woman, 2018). Testosterone shrinks breast cancer in animals as well.

I have heard from Dr. Glaser's breast cancer patients that she treats them with about three times the customary menopause testosterone subcutaneous pellet dosage—about three mg per pound. For reference, post-menopausal women receive a pellet dose of one mg per pound, which produces blood levels of 200 to 300 ng/dl. This makes most women feel great (recall my story about superwomen).

The usual pellet dose for a man is 10 mg per pound. This may produce blood levels of 1500 ng/dl. Weekly injections of inexpensive testosterone cypionate provide similar effects as pellets (finish this article in Hormone Secrets).

Rebecca Glaser, MD, has written many articles about testosterone treatment for breast cancer (website hormonebalance.org, link HERE). She also uses anastrozole, an estrogen blocker. (This last may not be optimal, and Cindy was taken off it by her current doctors.)

Cindy is currently using estradiol capsules 2 mg a day, progesterone capsules 200 mg twice a day, testosterone cream 200 mg/cc 1/2 cc a day, and DHEA 10 mg a day. Her testosterone levels are over 1500, the high-normal male range. This has suppressed and possibly cured her cancer.

Note: Cindy now weighs about 110 pounds. Bigger people may need higher testosterone doses to get blood levels this high.

SUBSTACK LINK

To find a doctor, contact Dr. Glaser, search *Hormone Secrets*, or see worldlinkmedical.com.

References from hormonebalance.org

Testosterone Implant Therapy in Women With and Without Breast Cancer. Androgen. 2021;2:94-110

Testosterone therapy in women: Myths and misconceptions. Maturitas. 2013;74:230-234

Beneficial effects of testosterone therapy in women measured by the validated Menopause Rating Scale (MRS). Maturitas. 2011;68:355-361

Testosterone Implants in Women: Pharmacological Dosing for a Physiologic Effect. Maturitas. 2013;74:179-184

Subcutaneous Testosterone Anastrozole Therapy in Men: Rationale, Dosing, and Levels on Therapy. Int J Pharm Compd. 2019;23:325-339

Incidence of invasive breast cancer in women treated with testosterone implants: a prospective 10-year cohort study. BMC Cancer. 2019;19:1271.

Incidence of invasive breast cancer in women treated with testosterone implants: a prospective 10-year cohort study. BMC Cancer. 2019;19:1271. Supplement 1. Statistical Methods

A randomized, double-blind, placebo-controlled trial of testosterone for treatment of postmenopausal women with aromatase inhibitor-induced arthralgias: Alliance study A221102. Supportive Care in Cancer. 20201-10

Breast cancer treatment in women over the age of 80: A tailored approach. Maturitas. 2018;110:29-32

Subcutaneous testosterone-letrozole therapy before and concurrent with neoadjuvant breast chemotherapy: clinical response and therapeutic implications. Menopause. 24, 7, 859-864

Effect of testosterone therapy on the female voice. Climacteric. 2016;19:2;198

Testosterone and breast cancer prevention. Maturitas. 2015;81:104

Rapid response of breast cancer to neoadjuvant intra-mammary testosterone-anastrozole therapy: neoadjuvant hormone therapy in breast cancer. Menopause (New York, NY). 2014;21:673

Efficacy of subcutaneous testosterone on menopausal symptoms in breast cancer survivors. ASCO. J Clin Oncol. 2014 Sep 10;32(Suppl 2):109

Reduced breast cancer incidence in women treated with subcutaneous testosterone, or testosterone with anastrozole: a prospective, observational study. Maturitas. 2013;76:342-349

Improvement in scalp hair growth in androgen deficient women treated with testosterone: a questionnaire study. British Journal of Dermatology. 2012;166:274-278

Glaser R, Dimitrakakis C, Trimble N, Martin V. Testosterone pellet implants and migraine headaches: a pilot study. Maturitas. 2012;71:385-388

Low salivary testosterone levels in patients with breast cancer. BMC cancer. 2010;10:547

Safety of maternal testosterone therapy during breast feeding. International journal of pharmaceutical compounding. 2009;13:314

Pilot study: absorption and efficacy of multiple hormones delivered in a single cream applied to the mucous membranes of the labia and vagina. Gynecologic and obstetric investigation. 2008;66:111-118

Chapter 59
A Few of Rogan's Podcasts Are Required Listening, But Use Double Speed

To Joe Rogan's credit, he frequently interviews people who are brighter than he is. A few become condescending, and when they do, he can get defensive—he is, after all, one of the biggest celebrities on the planet. Rogan considers himself a classic liberal, but with all that is happening lately, he sees that they are off-course. He is on Spotify, a censored platform. Here are some of his best.

Peter McCullough, MD. (Also HERE), Rogan #1747. Despite my knowledge of medical corruption, I did not grasp the Covid frauds until I listened to Dr. McCullough. He said that inexpensive, well-known treatments could have prevented most deaths. I have listened to medical academics my whole career and can smell their truth or fakery. McCullough is the real thing.

Robert Epstein's podcast (Rogan #1768) about tech censorship is HERE. Google is the most powerful company in the world. It influences elections by altering search engine results. But Epstein is watching them, and they know it. Listen, and you will learn how to remain independent.

Comedian Bill Maher is freakishly influential. Some of my idiot physician friends told me that the news was not worth bothering with if they could not get it from his show. In this interview (#1804), he trashed medicine, big Pharma, and vaccines. Maher, a lifelong progressive, now questions their integrity and the propaganda.

Chapter 60
Interviews on Liberty Sation

These are a two part studio-produced dialog between host Bryce Eddy and myself about healthcare corruption.

Liberty Station is a Christian platform. Some of my close friends are Catholics or other faiths, and they all tell me I am a believer. I tell them that my primary ethical system is from Marcus Aurelius, whose reign ended in 180 AD. His Stoic ideas predate Jesus.

SUBSTACK LINK RUMBLE LINK

Meditations, the little book of Aurelius's maxims, is one

of five books that have been in continuous publication since the invention of the printing press in the mid-1400s. I have read it over and over and memorized parts.

I like the poetic quality of George Long's translation (45 cents on Amazon Kindle), but some people find the newer version by Gregory Hays easier to read.

Here are a few sample quotes from the Long edition:

> If thou workest at that which is before thee, following right reason seriously, vigorously, calmly, without allowing anything else to distract thee, but keeping thy divine part pure, as if thou shouldst be bound to give it back immediately; if thou holdest to this, expecting nothing, fearing nothing, but satisfied with thy present activity according to nature, and with heroic truth in every word and sound which thou utterest, thou wilt live happy. And there is no man who is able to prevent this.

> One man after burying another has been laid out dead, and another buries him; and all this in a short time. Hippocrates after curing many diseases himself fell sick and died.. and lice killed Socrates... What means all this? ...All human things are smoke, and nothing at all; and it is not for us, but for the gods, to settle whether we play the play out, or only a part of it. Pass then through this little space of time conformably to nature, and tend thy journey in content, just as an olive falls off when it is ripe, blessing nature who produced it, and thanking the tree on which it grew. ... Do not act as if thou wert going to live 10,000 years. While thou can, while you are able, be good.

> Look within. Within is the fountain of good, and it will ever bubble up, if thou wilt ever dig.

> Remind yourself that it is not the future or the past

which bears down on you but the present always the present which becomes an even smaller thing when isolated in this way.

It all depends on your opinion of it, and that depends on you. Jettison your opinion, and you will find yourself like a sailor rounding the headland on a calm sea in a bay without waves.

Bad luck borne nobly is good luck.

* * *

SECOND HOUR: Bryce admitted that he works for an insurance company. I gave him no slack about that.

SUBSTACK LINK

My host has over 25 years of experience doing Gracie JuJitsu and runs a competitive gym. He still "rolls" or competes with younger players. He has a neck as big as my Cane Corso's, and these dogs are like pit bulls on steroids.

The photo from the event below showcases my 2500 hair transplants. And yes, I dye every one of them. As for the yellow T-shirt, it was an attempt at personal style.

Cassandra's Memo

Chapter 61
The BS-Free MDs Treat Covid Safely

Family practitioners May and Tim Hindmarsh made it through the pandemic and saw a lot of sick patients. Many came from other states because their medical practice was the only one in the region to treat Covid properly. They use safe nutraceuticals and effective monoclonal antibodies.

SUBSTACK LINK

Intravenous antibodies require only a brief clinic visit. They told me that if they gave the treatment within a day or two of the start of symptoms, it usually cured the disease.

They also said the antibody type that should be used is unique for each Covid variant. In other words, the Omicron treatment does not work for Delta and vice versa.

These doctors are two hours north of Portland, Oregon, and you can listen to their practice podcasts HERE.

The couple is a little goofy but super nice and brilliant clinicians.

Chapter 62
Nick Yaya Asks Peter Breggin
About His Book

Nick does a charming podcast interviewing Peter Breggin, MD. He and his wife Ginger wrote the best early book about the global situation, *COVID 19 and the Global Predators: We are the Prey*. It has 1260 Amazon reviews, almost all 5-star.

SUBSTACK LINK

Chapter 63
Maajid Nawaz, Retired Terrorist

Maajid Nawaz is a charismatic man with riveting perspectives. Although he describes a hero's path for us, I am uncertain about his story. He denies current establishment ties but has worked with many evil actors. Since I am not an expert on politics, international relations, or recent history outside of medicine, I would like my readers to let me know what they think.

This is a guest interview from Peter McCormack's What Bitcoin Did *podcast, the best introduction to Bitcoin. I have listened to many of his episodes and am using this interview with his kind permission. HERE is the link to the original discussion. I recorded this at 1.25 speed.*

Nawaz is a British Pakistani who was a leader in an Islamist group. In December 2001, when he was 20 years old, he was arrested in Egypt. Although nonviolent, he was sentenced to five years in prison for promoting his radical ideas and was thrown in with some of the most notorious criminals in the Middle East. Some others serving time with him were just university professors advocating change.

445

(Wikipedia)

When he was not in solitary confinement or being forced to watch others being tortured with electric shocks on their genitals, he studied. He learned enough from the other prisoners to get the equivalent of several degrees in international relations. Nawaz became convinced that the violent Islamist approach was a mistake, and when he was released from prison at 28, he renounced the extremist group.

Luckily, his former colleagues decided not to kill him. He became a commentator and consultant and now, at 43, is a prominent critic of Islamism. He has testified before Congress. He knows George Bush, David Cameron, and was a senior advisor to Tony Blair. He trained the FBI, CIA, and similar British agencies. He has been on the Joe Rogan show. Lately, he has been labeled a "conspiracy theorist" and censored for telling the truth about Covid.

Cassandra's Memo

Nawaz said he met many sincere underlings in the British and US government service. But he believes that all regimes and government agencies hoard power and end up as corrupt tools of the powerful. After his experiences, Nawaz concluded that interference with the free flow of information had profoundly evil effects. He says that the best protection the world has now is the US Constitution.

Chapter 64
Interview With Chris Bray

C hris is a fantastic writer and former journalist who taught history at a university. His Substack title is "Tell Me How This Ends."

SUBSTACK LINK

Here are a few things we discussed.

✪ The entire middle of the country missed the pandemic.

✪ How Google suggests search results that dictate the Agenda.

✪ How "the dismal California Legislature, following a

well-established state tradition, slopped a giant bucket of sewage into the sausage-making pipeline this year."

✪ "In less than a decade, Stanford's administration eviscerated a hundred years of undergraduate culture and social groups..."

✪ About that photo of Biden looking like Hitler with the red background.

✪ Research fraud for Alzheimer's drugs. "You can cheat to get a paper. You can cheat to get a degree. You can cheat to get a grant. You can't cheat to cure a disease... Biology doesn't care."

✪ The degenerate "Little Demon" Disney cartoon about Satan and his daughter.

✪ "The frantic institutional efforts to strangle this knowledge will not overcome what people see right in front of their faces. The truth isn't coming out — the truth is out. Institutions and organizations, like the "expert" panels that make vaccine recommendations to the FDA, can't overcome this reality."

✪ Quoting an "expert" who is normalizing pedophilia:

Some of you may mistakenly think that it's wrong or bad to be an adult who wants to f*** children, but as a licensed clinician with a professional background and deep training in this field, let me assure you that you are mistaken. If you oppose my redefinition, you oppose expertise; you are, as an untrained layman, contradicting my specialized professional knowledge. You are operating outside of your knowledge, assuming things that you aren't qualified to assert. You have to accept... my specialized knowledge and my professional standing as a credentialed expert.

Robert Yoho, MD (ret)

✪ The plague of people who do not read:

I remain extremely confident that the flood of bullshit like this is being slopped out by people who DRS — who Don't Read S*** — about the topic they cover. Somebody in a government agency shot this dude an email message that said COVID VACCINES ARE MIRACLE DRUGS EVERYONE SHOULD GET THEM, and he said to himself, "Miracle drugs, got it!" We're plagued by an army of people who pour "information" into the world based on two Twitter posts and a text message after a full three to five seconds of deep thought.

Chapter 65
"Joan Of Arc" Amelia Escapes From Canadian Alcatraz

Amelia had an ordinary life in Quebec, Canada, until 2020. She had many friends, owned a successful business, and had the love and support of a large family. She was at a stage when most women get married and start families.

Amelia is an empathic person whose strength is intuition and feeling. Although she has a college degree, she is not an intellectual, and English is her second language. But in mid-2021, when the vaccine mandates began in Canada, she began to feel a growing evil.

She knew the vaccine was not for her, but as she tried to lead her simple life, she was attacked from all sides. Her relatives expelled her, and the electric shocks of their disapproval painfully injured her. She had a brief experience of unreality and was kidnapped by psychiatrists for three days. After escaping, she gave away her business, traveled to Mexico for a month, and settled in Miami into a new life.

French women started movements and led their nation. Amelia is no Joan, but her convictions are powerful. Listen as she relates her visions of the Covid disaster. She says she left Quebec at the last moment.

SUBSTACK LINK

Please stay in touch

I hope we now have a relationship. Please subscribe at robertyoho.substack.com, and I will email you more content weekly.

Do not forget to write reviews of my books. I will read them, and I appreciate you for doing it. Reviewing a book before finishing it is acceptable. You can update what you say later if you want. If this is an ebook, click this LINK to review *Butchered by "Healthcare"*, this LINK to review *Hormone Secrets*. Amazon censored this book, so please write your reviews (thank you!) on other platforms such as Google, Kobo, Apple, or Barnes and Noble.

Email: Yoho.Robert@gmail.com. Mailing address: 99 West California Blvd #50007, Pasadena, CA 91115.

Professional CV: Current

✪ 69 years old (2022). Retired from medical practice in 2019.

✪ Writer and whistleblower for over five years.

✪ Topics: censorship, the Constitution, medical corruption, and the global psychopaths.

✪ Website: RobertYohoAuthor.com and RobertYoho.substack.com.

Professional CV: Past

✪ Emergency medicine career out of medical school.

✪ American Board of Emergency Medicine: passed board exams and twice re-certified.

✪ Practiced for three decades as a cosmetic surgeon, (see DrYoho.com).

✪ American Society of Cosmetic Breast Surgery: fellow, trustee, officer, and past president.

✪ American Board of Cosmetic Surgery: passed board exams and twice re-certified.

✪ Fellow, American Academy of Cosmetic Surgery (inactive).

455

❂ New Body Cosmetic Surgery Center: founder & director (inactive).

❂ American Association Ambulatory Health Care (AAAHC) accredited surgical/medical practice for over 25 years (inactive).

Climber CV (This is unimpressive in 2023)

❂ El Capitan, Half Dome (Yosemite): 24-hour ascents

❂ Free ascents of Astroman (11.c) and Crucifix (12.a)

❂ First ascents in Yosemite, Joshua Tree, Devil's Tower

❂ Solo ascents to 5.10c

After an ascent of Yosemite's El Capitan in 26 hours. Grant Horner (left) later solo-climbed the North Face of the Eiger without a rope.

Books by Robert Yoho

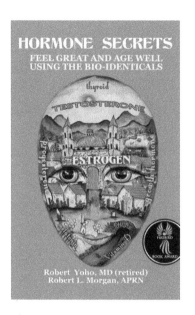

HORMONE SECRETS
FEEL GREAT AND AGE WELL USING THE BIO-IDENTICALS

thyroid
TESTOSTERONE
progesterone
ESTROGEN
DHEA
Vitamin

Robert Yoho, MD (retired)
Robert L. Morgan, APRN

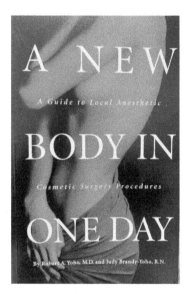

A NEW
A Guide to Local Anesthetic

BODY IN
Cosmetic Surgery Procedures

ONE DAY
By Robert A. Yoho, M.D. and Judy Brandy-Yoho, R.N.

Printed in the USA
CPSIA information can be obtained
at www.ICGtesting.com
LVHW052109061023
760219LV00061B/565